SILVER·BURDETT

Making
Music

Keyboard
Accompaniments

Teacher's Edition Part Two
Grade 3

PEARSON

Scott
Foresman

Editorial Offices: Glenview, Illinois • Parsippany, New Jersey • New York, New York
Sales Offices: Parsippany, New Jersey • Duluth, Georgia • Glenview, Illinois
Coppell, Texas • Ontario, California • Mesa, Arizona
ISBN: 0-328-07773-9
Copyright © 2005, Pearson Education, Inc.

4 5 6 7 8 9 10 V039 13 12 11 10 09 08 07 06 05

Contents

Accompaniments 4

Song Index 191

To the Teacher

Keyboard accompaniments are provided for those songs for which the keyboard is an appropriate instrument or a reasonable substitute for authentic instruments.

The triangle-shaped boxes within an accompaniment designate the beginnings of lines of music on the student page. Harmonies in an accompaniment may differ from those on the recording and from the chord symbols in the student text.

Hello to All the Children of the World

Words by Nancy Klein

Music by Nancy Klein and Pam Beall
Arranged by Georgette LeNorth

REFRAIN

Hel - lo, Bon-jour, Bue-nos dí-as, G' - day, Gu - ten Tag, Kon - ni - chi

wa. Ciao, Sha - lom, Do - brey dy - en, Hel - lo to all the chil - dren of the

Fine VERSE

world!

1. We live in dif - f'rent plac - es from
2. There's chil - dren in the des - erts, and

all a - round the world. We speak in man - y dif - f'rent ways.__ Though
chil - dren in the towns And chil - dren who live by the sea.__ If

D.C. al Fine

some things might be dif - f'rent, we're child - ren just the same, And
we could meet each oth - er to run and sing and play, then

we all like to sing and play.
what good friends we all could be.

Supercalifragilisticexpialidocious

Words and Music by Richard M. Sherman and Robert B. Sherman
Arranged by Ting Ho

5 **6**

p Um did-dle did-didle did-dle, um did-dle ay! Um did-dle did-dle did-dle, um did-dle ay!

7 **8**

mf 1. Be - cause I was a - fraid to speak when I was just a lad, Me

9

fa - ther gave me nose a tweak and told me I was bad. But

10

then one day I learned a word that saved me ach - in' nose, The

D.S. al Fine

big - gest word you ev - er 'eard and this is 'ow it goes; Oh!

2. 'E traveled all around the world and ev'rywhere 'e went
   E'd use his word and all would say, "There goes a clever gent!"
   When dukes and maharajas pass the time of day with me,
   I say me special word and then they ask me out to tea. Oh! *Refrain*

3. So when the cat has got your tongue, there's no need for dismay.
   Just summon up this word and then you've got a lot to say.
   But better use it carefully or it can change your life.
   One night I said it to me girl and now me girl's me wife. Oh! *Refrain*

Gypsy in the Moonlight

Folk Song from Trinidad
Arranged by Marilyn J. Patterson

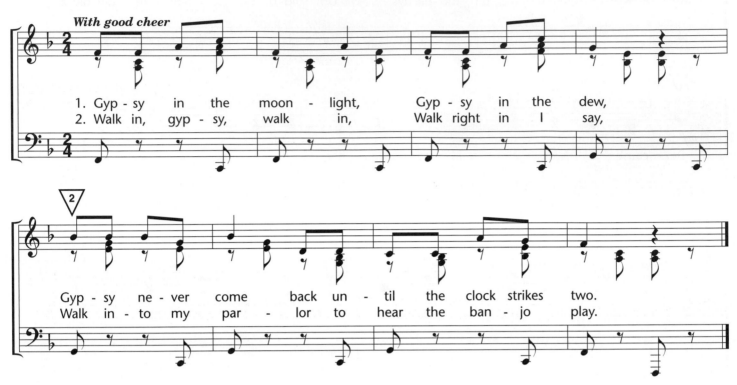

1. Gyp - sy in the moon - light, Gyp - sy in the dew,
2. Walk in, gyp - sy, walk in, Walk right in I say,

Gyp - sy ne - ver come back un - til the clock strikes two.
Walk in - to my par - lor to hear the ban - jo play.

3. I don't want nobody,
   Nobody wants me,
   All I want is Mary
   to come and dance with me.

4. Tra-la-la . . .

Ding, Dong, Diggidiggidong

English Version Adapted from Orff-Schulwerk by Margaret Murray

From Orff-Keetman, Orff-Schulwerk, Vol. 1
Arranged by Carol Jay

Ding, dong, dig - gi - dig - gi - dong, Dig - gi - dig - gi - dong, the cat she's gone.

Golden Ring Around Susan Girl

Folk Song from the Appalachian Mountains
as sung by Jean Ritchie
Arranged by Cheryl Terhune Cronk

Au clair de la lune *(In the Moonlight)*

English Version by D. Auberge

Traditional Song from France
Arranged by Carol Jay

The accompaniment for this song is found on p. 13. *Ambos a dos*

Joy to the World

Words and Music by Hoyt Axton
Arranged by Polly Carder

Ambos a dos *(Go Two by Two)*

English words by Aura Kontra

Folk Song from Latin America
Arranged by Rosemary Jacques

2. *¿Dónde están las llaves?. . .*
   ¿Dónde están las llaves?. . .

2. Where's the key to the door?. . .
   Where's the key to the door?. . .

I Don't Care If the Rain Comes Down

Traditional Folk Song from the United States
Arranged by Carol Jay

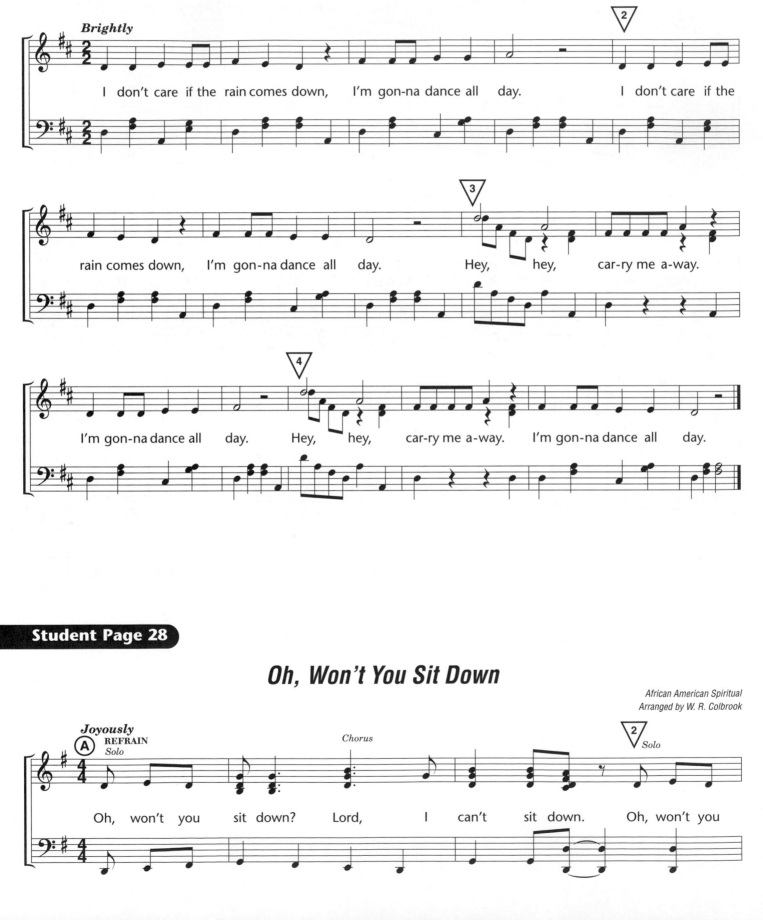

Oh, Won't You Sit Down

African American Spiritual
Arranged by W. R. Colbrook

2. Who's that yonder dressed in blue?
   Must be the children that are comin' through.
   Who's that yonder dressed in black?
   Must be the hypocrites a-turnin' back. *Refrain.*

Ida Red

Folk Song from Kentucky
Arranged by Buddy Skipper

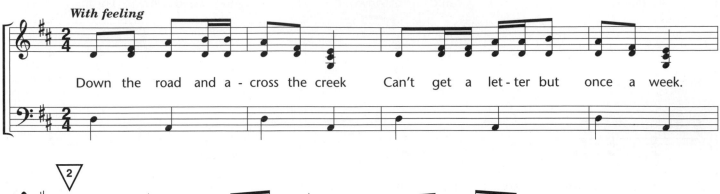

Down the road and a - cross the creek   Can't get a let - ter but once a week.

I - da Red   I - da Blue   I got stuck on I - da, too.

Mud

Words by Marilyn Singer

Music by David Eddleman

This stick here,   that stick there.___   Mud, more mud, add

Make New Friends

Traditional Round
Arranged by Marilyn Christensen

Make new friends, but keep the old.

One is sil - ver and the oth - er gold.

La pulga de San José

Adapted Spanish Words by José-Luis Orozco

Musical arrangement by José-Luis Orozco
Folk Song from Latin America
Piano accompaniment by Rosemary Jacques

1. En la pul-ga de San Jo-sé yo com-pré u-na gui-ta-rra,

ta-ra, ta-ra, ta-rra, la gui-ta-rra. Va-ya u-sted, va-ya u-sted a la

pul-ga de San jo-sé.

2. En la pulga de San José,
   yo compré un clarinete,
   nete, nete, nete, el clarinete,
   tara, tara, tarra, la guitarra. Refrain

3. En la pulga de San José,
   yo compré un violín,
   lín, lín, lín, el violín,
   nete, nete, nete, el clarinete,
   tara, tara, tarra, la guitarra. Refrain

Peppermint Twist

Words and Music by Henry Glover and Joey Dee
Arranged by Buddy Skipper

Rhythmically

They got a new dance and it goes like this.__ The
Meet__ me pal down on forty-fifth street,__

name of the dance is the Pep-per-mint Twist.__
Where the__ Pepper-mint__ Twist-ers meet.__

Well you'll like_____ it like this,__ the Pep-per-mint Twist.
And you'll learn_____ to do this,__ the Pep-per-mint Twist.

Well, 'round and 'round, up and down,

'round   and   'round   up   and   down

'round and 'round and   up and down   one two three kick   one, two, three jump.

Well, al - right____   all

night__   well, al-right.   It's o - kay,____   all

Train Is A-Comin'

African American Spiritual
Arranged by Buddy Skipper

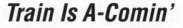

3. Room for many others, oh, yes,
Room for many others, oh, yes,
Room for many others, room for many others,
Room for many others, oh, yes.

Black Snake

Traditional
Arranged by Bill Wallace

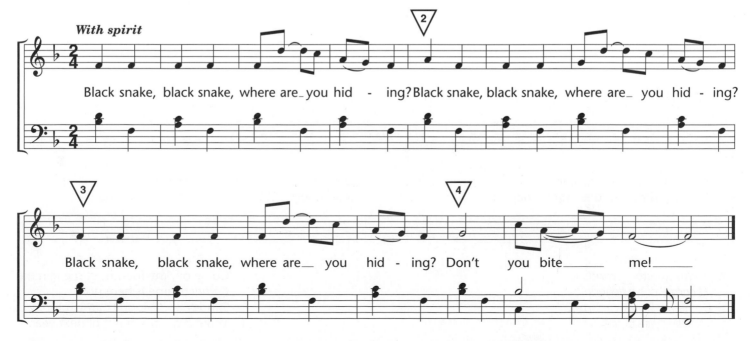

Mister Ram Goat-O

Folk Song from Trinidad
Arranged by Buddy Skipper

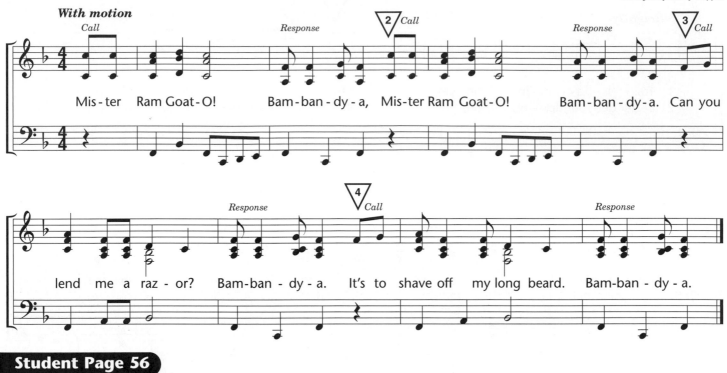

Mis-ter Ram Goat-O! Bam-ban-dy-a, Mis-ter Ram Goat-O! Bam-ban-dy-a. Can you

lend me a raz-or? Bam-ban-dy-a. It's to shave off my long beard. Bam-ban-dy-a.

Ahora voy a cantarles *(Now Hear the Song)*

English Words by Alice Firgau

Folk Song from Argentina
Arranged by Joyce Kalbach

1. Aho-ra voy a can-tar-les has-ta que a-pun-te el lu-ce-ro.
1. Now hear the song I'll sing you Un-til the dawn is___ break-ing.

Los car-na-va-les ya vie-nen des-de la ci-ma del ce-rro.
All through the night hap-py peo-ple Come down from on the___ moun-tain.

2. ¡Todos, toditos, arriba!
¡El carnaval ha llegado!
Domingo, lunes y martes,
Tres días y se acabó.

2. Come on, my friends, come join me
Carnaval time is here now,
Sunday and Monday and Tuesday,
Three days, no more 'til next year.

Great Day

African American Spiritual
Arranged by Don Kalbach

John Kanaka

Sea Shanty
Arranged by Georgette LeNorth

The Loco-Motion

Words and Music by Gerry Goffin and Carole King
Arranged by Mary Jean Nelson

One Morning Soon *The accompaniment for this song is found on p. 30.*

Family Tree

Words and Music by John Forster and Tom Chapin
Arranged by Jill Gallina

Humorously

1. Be - fore the days of Jell - O lived a pre - his - tor - ic
2. My grand - pa came from Rus - sia; my grand - ma came from
3. One fine day I may go to Tie - rra del

fel - low Who loved a maid and court - ed her be - neath the ban - yan
Prus - sia; They met in No - va Sco - tia, had my dad in Ten - nes -
Fue - go. Per - haps I'll meet my wife there and we'll move to Tim - buk -

tree. And they had lots of chil - dren and their chil - dren all had
see. Then they moved to Yo - ko - ha - ma, where Dad - dy met my
tu. And our kid will be bi - lin - gual, and though she may stay

chil - dren. And they kept on hav - ing chil - dren un - til one of them had
ma - ma. Her___ dad's from Al - a - bam - a and her mom's part Cher - o -
sin - gle, She___ could, of course, go min - gle with the king of Kat - man -

me. We're a fam - 'ly and we're a
kee.
du.

tree. Our roots go deep down in___ his - to -

ry, From my great - great - grand - dad - dy reach - in' up to me;___

We're a green and grow - ing___ fam - 'ly tree.

One Morning Soon

African American Spiritual
Arranged by John Girt

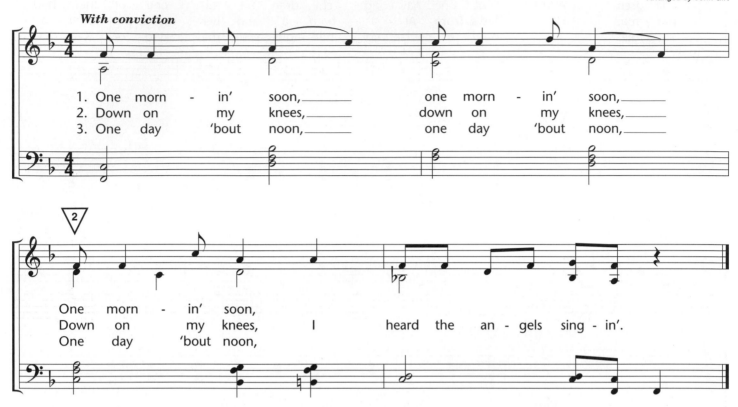

With conviction

1. One morn - in' soon,_____ one morn - in' soon,_____
2. Down on my knees,_____ down on my knees,_____
3. One day 'bout noon,_____ one day 'bout noon,_____

One morn - in' soon,
Down on my knees, I heard the an - gels sing - in'.
One day 'bout noon,

I'm on My Way

African American Spiritual
Arranged by Rosemary Jacques

With a lift

1. I'm on my way (I'm on my way) to the free-dom land, (to the free-dom land,) I'm on my

way (I'm on my way) to the free-dom land, (to the free-dom land,) I'm on my way (I'm on my

way) to the free-dom land, (to the free-dom land,) I'm on my way,_ thank God, I'm on my way._____

2. I asked my friends. . . to go with me, *(3 times)*
I'm on my way, thank God, I'm on my way.

3. If they won't come. . . then I'll go alone, *(3 times)*
I'm on my way, thank God, I'm on my way.

4. I'm on my way,. . . and I won't turn back, *(3 times)*
I'm on my way, thank God, I'm on my way.

Old Texas

Cowboy Song from Oklahoma
Arranged by George Douglass

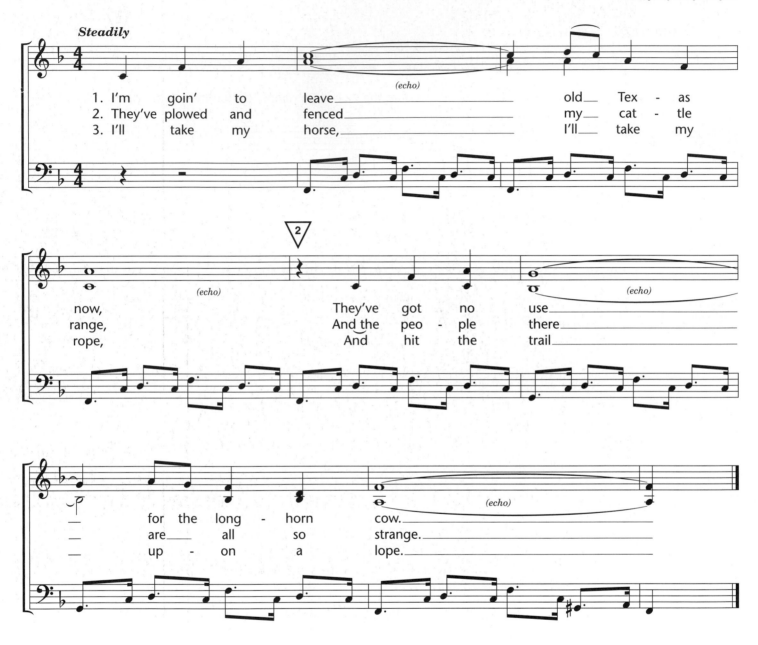

4. Say *adiós* to the Alamo
   And turn my head t'ward Mexico.

Hej pada pada (Dewdrops)

English Words by Ellen K. Traeger

Lullaby from Slovakia
Arranged by Betsy Washington

Tenderly

Hej pa - da pa - da ro - sič - ka, Spa - ly by mo - je
Dew - drops a - fall - ing from the skies, Drow - sy and sleep - y,

o - čič - ka. Spa - ly by mo - je, Spa - ly by aj tvo - je,
close your eyes. Drow - sy and sleep - y, go to sleep my ba - by.

Spa - ly by du - ša mo - ja o - bo - je.
Dream of the dew - drops fall - ing from the skies.

33

Let's Get the Rhythm of the Band

Based on a Children's Rhyme

New Words and Music by Cheryl Warren Mattox
Arranged by John Girt

34

El gallo pinto (The Painted Rooster)

English Words by Jorge Winston-La Paz

Spanish words and Music by Tita Maya
Arranged by W. R. Colbrook

El ga - llo pin - to no pin - ta, El que pin - ta es el pin -
The paint-ed roos - ter's no paint - er, For the paint - er's the one who

tor Que al ga - llo pin - to las pin - tas Pin - ta por pin - ta pin - tó.
paints; The one who paint-ed that roos - ter Paint - ed each feath-er so quaint.

Kingston Market

Words and Music by Irving Burgie
Arranged by Paul Somers

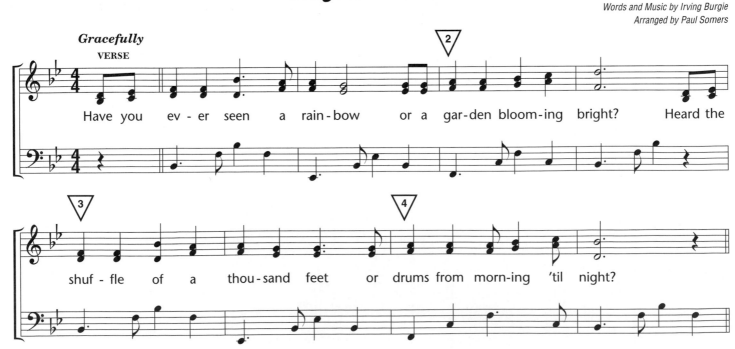

Have you ev - er seen a rain - bow or a gar - den bloom-ing bright? Heard the

shuf - fle of a thou-sand feet or drums from morn-ing 'til night?

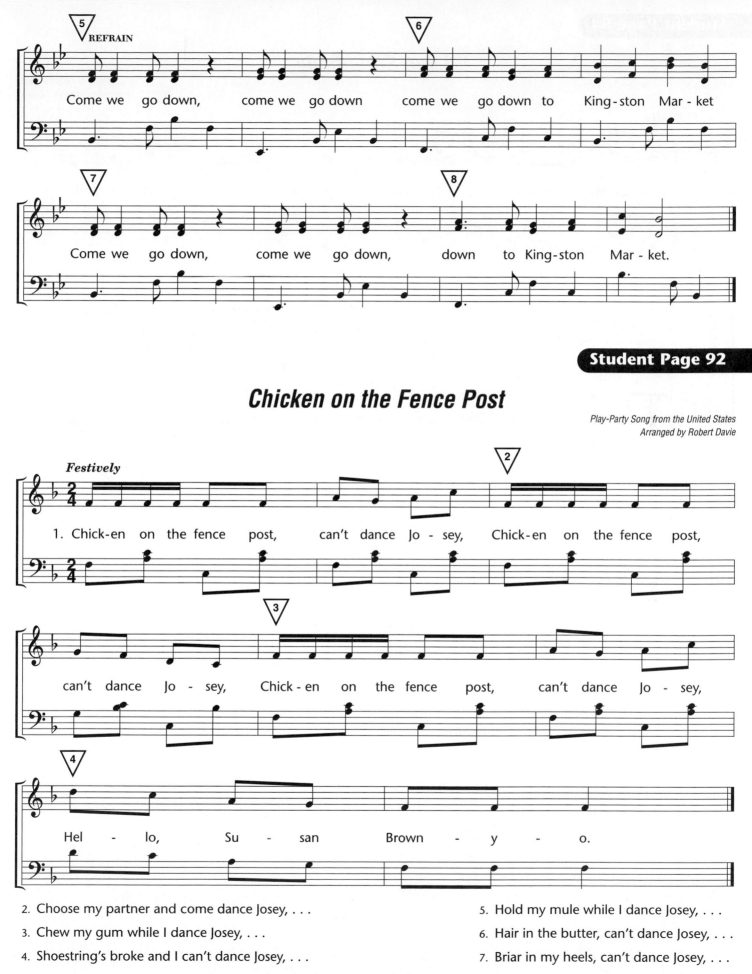

Chicken on the Fence Post

Play-Party Song from the United States
Arranged by Robert Davie

Festively

1. Chick-en on the fence post, can't dance Jo - sey, Chick-en on the fence post,

can't dance Jo - sey, Chick - en on the fence post, can't dance Jo - sey,

Hel - lo, Su - san Brown - y - o.

2. Choose my partner and come dance Josey, . . .

3. Chew my gum while I dance Josey, . . .

4. Shoestring's broke and I can't dance Josey, . . .

5. Hold my mule while I dance Josey, . . .

6. Hair in the butter, can't dance Josey, . . .

7. Briar in my heels, can't dance Josey, . . .

8. Stumped my toe, can't dance Josey, . . .

Love Somebody

Folk Song from the Unted States
Arranged by Rosemary Jacques

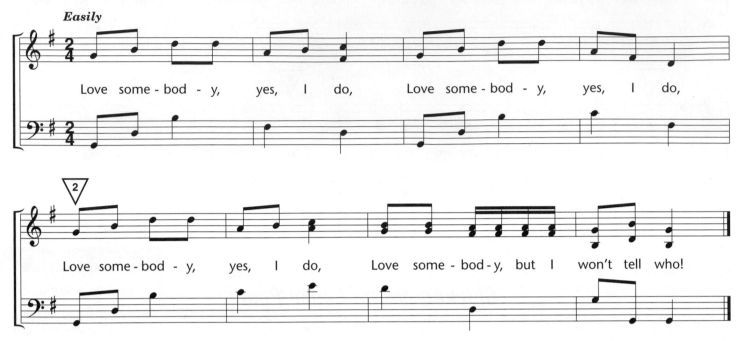

Love some-bod-y, yes, I do, Love some-bod-y, yes, I do,

Love some-bod-y, yes, I do, Love some-bod-y, but I won't tell who!

Old Dan Tucker

Folk Song from the United States
Arranged by Scott Garrison

1. Old Dan Tuck-er was a might-y man, He washed his face in the fry-ing pan,
2. Old Dan Tuck - er___ came to town, Rid-ing a billy goat,__ lead-ing a hound;

Combed his hair with a wag - on wheel, Had a tooth-ache in his heel.
Hound dog barked, then__ billy goat jumped; Dan fell off and landed on a stump.

So get out the way, Old Dan Tuck - er; Get out the way, Old Dan Tuck - er;

Get out the way, Old Dan Tuck - er, You're too late to get your sup - per.

Never Smile at a Crocodile

Words by Jack Lawrence

Music by Frank Churchill
Arranged by Buddy Skipper

Light and Bouncy

Nev - er smile at a croc - o - dile, No, you can't get friend-ly with a croc - o - dile, Don't be

tak - en in by his wel - come grin, He's im - ag - in - ing how well you'd fit with - in his skin.

Nev - er smile at a croc - o - dile, Nev - er tip your hat and stop to talk a while. 1.,2. Nev - er
3. Don't be

run, walk a - way, say "Good - night," not "Good day!" Clear the aisle and nev - er smile at Mis - ter
rude, nev - er mock, throw a kiss, not a rock.

Fine

Croc - o - dile. You may ve - ry well be well - bred, Lots of et - i - quette in your head,

But there's al-ways some spe-cial case, time or place to for-get et-i-quette.

Student Page 102

Hwa yuan li-de young wa wa (Garden Lullaby)

Words by Po-Yang Chou
English Words by Ellen Williams

Music by Chuen-Taur Su
Arranged by Joyce Kalbach

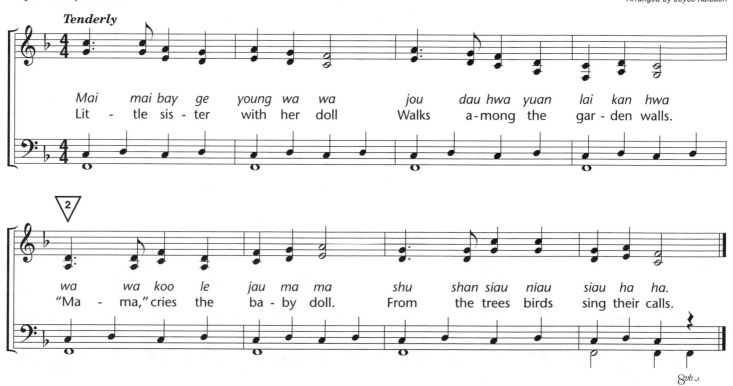

Tenderly

Mai mai bay ge young wa wa jou dau hwa yuan lai kan hwa
Lit - tle sis - ter with her doll Walks a-mong the gar - den walls.

wa wa koo le jau ma ma shu shan siau niau siau ha ha.
"Ma - ma," cries the ba - by doll. From the trees birds sing their calls.

41

Alabama Gal

Folk Song from Alabama
Arranged by Judith C. Lane

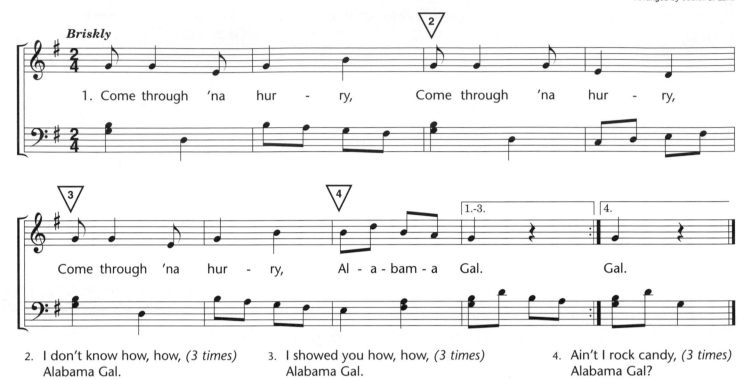

2. I don't know how, how, *(3 times)*
Alabama Gal.

3. I showed you how, how, *(3 times)*
Alabama Gal.

4. Ain't I rock candy, *(3 times)*
Alabama Gal?

Old Man Mosie

Singing Game from the United States
Arranged by Edward F. Corson

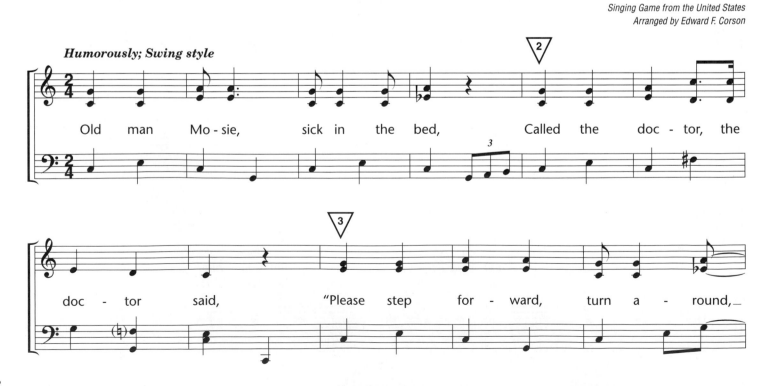

Do the ho - key po - key, and get out of town."

Had To Get Up This Mornin' Soon

African American Song
Arranged by Marilyn J. Patterson

Had to get up this morn-in' soon, Had to get up this morn - in' soon, Had to

get up this morn - in' soon, soon, Had to get up this morn - in' soon.

1. Woke up this morn-in' in such big haste, I did - n't have time to wash my face.
2. Got up this morn-in' an got up so soon, I could-n't see nothin' but the stars and moon.

Fine

D.C. al Fine

Tender Shepherd

Words by Carolyn Leigh

Music by Mark Charlap
Arranged by Rosemary Jacques

The Groundhog Blues

Words and Music by Gayle Giese
Arranged by Edward Corson

Draw Me a Bucket of Water

African American Singing Game
Arranged by Carol Jay

Written and adapted by Bessie Jones. Collected and edited by Alan Lomax. TRO-© Copyright 1972 (Renewed) Ludlow Music, Inc., New York, New York. Used by permission.

Frog in the buck - et and I can't get him out.

Repeat 1 time

Student Page 128

Morning Is Come

Round from England
Arranged by Francis Girard

Morn - ing is come, night is a - way, Rise with the

sun_____ and_____ wel - come the day.

47

The Juniper Tree

Folk Song from Arkansas
Arranged by Ting Ho

1. Oh, sis - ter Pheo - be, how mer - ry were we, The night we sat
2. Go choose a part - ner, so choose you a one, Go choose you the

un - der the jun - i - per tree, The jun - i - per tree, hi -
fair - est that ev - er you can. Now rise you up, gal and

o, hi - o, The jun - i - per tree, hi - o.
go, and go, Now rise you up gal and go.

"The Juniper Tree," copyright 1937 by John A. Lomax. Reprinted by permission of Global Jukebox Publishing.

¡Qué gusto! (What Pleasure)

English Words by Ruth DeCesare and Ellen Traeger

Hispanic Song of the American Southwest
Arranged by Marilyn J. Patterson

With gusto

¡Qué gus - to, qué
What pleas-ure, what

gus - to, qué gus - to me da, vi - vir en el cam - po con tran - qui - li -
plea - sure and joy it gives me To live in the coun - try, so peace - ful and

dad! Yo can - to, yo brin - co a mi li - ber - tad, por - que
free! I sing and I dance and I jump all a - round, Ver - y

no hay ti - je - ras de la so - cie - dad.
free of the crowds and the noise I once found.

49

Doong gul ge *('Round and Around We Go)*

English Words by Kim Williams

Korean Words and Music by Lee Su In
Arranged by Ting Ho

Doong gul ge doong gul ge,_____ doong gul ge doong gul ge,_____
'Round and a - round we go,_____ 'round and a - round we go!_____

bing gul bing gul dol ah kah miaw chum ul chup shi da._____
Dance a - round the cir - cle now, don't let your feet be slow._____

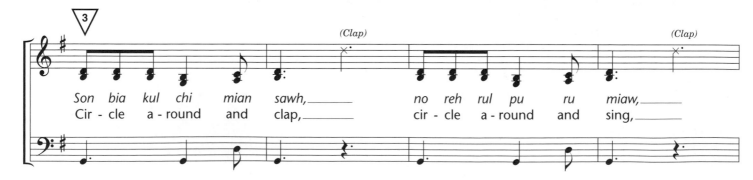

Son bia kul chi mian sawh,_____ no reh rul pu ru miaw,_____
Cir - cle a - round and clap,_____ cir - cle a - round and sing,_____

la la la la chul kaw up ge chum chu cha.
Let's all run to - ge - ther now a - round the ring!

Ring - a - ring - a - ring_____ a - ring - a - ring - a - ring,
Ring - a - ring - a - ring_____ a - ring - a - ring - a - ring,

ring - a - ring - a - ring_____ a - ring - a - ring - a - ring.
ring - a - ring - a - ring_____ a - ring - a - ring - a - ring.

Son eh son ul chah(p)_____ go mo du da hahm ge,
Hop - ping as we go_____ and jump - ing as we sing,

chul kaw up ge chum ul chup shi da._____
Let's all run to - gether - er 'round the ring!_____

51

Kum bachur atzel (Hear the Rooster Crowing)

English Words by David ben Avraham

Folk Song from Israel
Arranged by Elaine C. Thomas

Li'l Liza Jane

Dance Song from the United States
Arranged by Bernhard Heiden

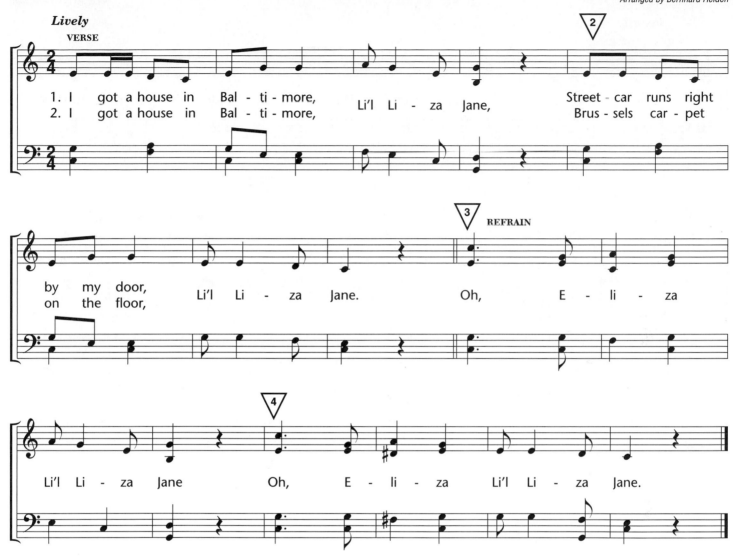

3. I got a house in Baltimore, . . .
   Silver doorplate on the door, . . .

4. Come, my love, and be with me, . . .
   And I'll take good care of thee, . . .

Hop Up, My Ladies

Folk Song from the United States
Arranged by Francis Girard

Steadily

VERSE

1. Did you ev-er go to meet-ing, Un-cle Joe, Un-cle Joe? Did you

ev-er go to meet-ing, Un-cle Joe? ___ Did you ev-er go to

meet-ing Un-cle Joe, Un-cle Joe? I don't mind the weath-er, if the

REFRAIN

wind don't blow. Hop up, my la-dies, three in a row,

Collected, adapted and arranged by John A. Lomax and Alan Lomax. TRO © copyright 1941 (Renewed) Ludlow Music, Inc., New York, N.Y. Used by permission.

2. Will your horse carry double,
   Uncle Joe, Uncle Joe? . . .
   Refrain

3. Is your horse a single footer,
   Uncle Joe, Uncle Joe? . . .
   Refrain

Walk Together, Children

African American Spiritual
Arranged by Joseph Joubert

1. Oh, walk to - geth - er, chil - dren, Don't you get___ wea - ry,
2. Oh, talk to - geth - er, chil - dren, Don't you get___ wea - ry,

Walk to - geth - er, chil - dren, Don't you get wea - ry, Oh,
Talk to - geth - er, chil - dren, Don't you get wea - ry, Oh,

walk to - geth - er, chil - dren, Don't you get___ wea - ry, There's a
talk to - geth - er, chil - dren, Don't you get___ wea - ry, There's a

great camp - meet - ing in the prom - ised land.___
great camp - meet - ing in the prom - ised land.___

3. Oh, sing together, children, . . .

4. Oh, shout together, children, . . .

This Old Man

Folk Song From England
Arranged by Bruce Simpson

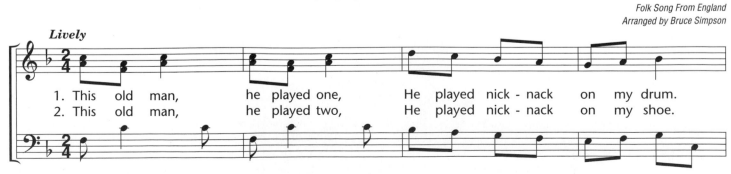

1. This old man, he played one, He played nick - nack on my drum.
2. This old man, he played two, He played nick - nack on my shoe.

Nick - nack, pad - dy whack, give the dog a bone, This old man came roll - ing home.

3. This old man, he played three,
He played nick-nack on my tree.

4. This old man, he played four,
He played nick-nack on my door.

5. This old man, he played five,
He played nick-nack on my hive.

6. This old man, he played six,
He played nick-nack on my sticks.

7. This old man, he played seven,
He played nick-nack on my oven.

8. This old man, he played eight,
He played nick-nack on my gate.

9. This old man, he played nine,
He played nick-nack on my line.

10. This old man, he played ten,
He played nick-nack on my hen.

Student Page 153

Michael Finnigan

Traditional from the United States
Arranged by Joyce Kalbach

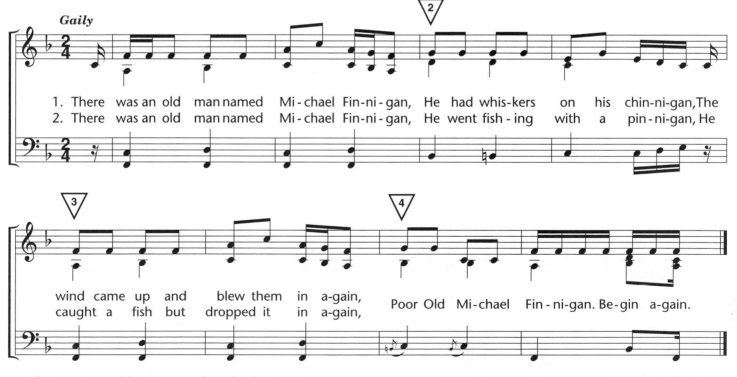

1. There was an old man named Mi - chael Fin - ni - gan, He had whis - kers on his chin - ni - gan, The
2. There was an old man named Mi - chael Fin - ni - gan, He went fish - ing with a pin - ni - gan, He

wind came up and blew them in a-gain,
caught a fish but dropped it in a-gain,
Poor Old Mi - chael Fin - ni - gan. Be - gin a - gain.

3. There was an old man named Michael Finnigan,
Climbed a tree and barked his shinnigan,
He lost about a yard of skinnigan,
Poor old Michael Finnigan. Begin again.

4. There was an old man named Michael Finnigan,
He grew fat and then grew thinnigan,
Then he died and had to begin again,
Poor old Michael Finnigan. Begin again.

Each of Us Is a Flower

Words and Music by Charlotte Diamond
Arranged by Don Kalbach

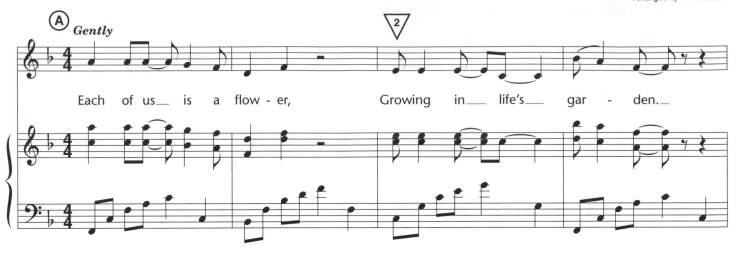

Each of us__ is a flow - er, Growing in__ life's__ gar - den.__

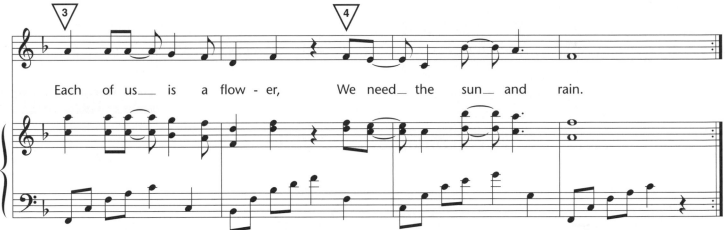

Each of us__ is a flow - er, We need__ the sun__ and rain.

Sun,_____ shine your warmth on__ me. Moon,_____ cool me

with your   night.   Wind,_________ bring the gen - tle____ rain.

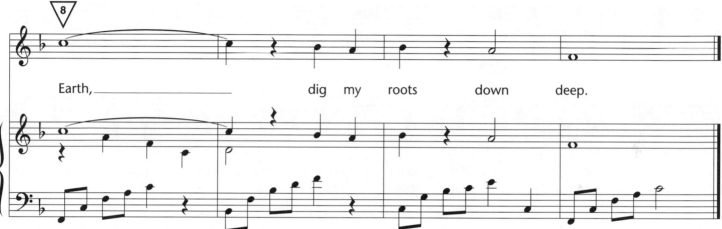

Earth,______________ dig my roots down deep.

The Flat Foot Floogee

Words and Music by Slim Gaillard, Slam Stewart, and Bud Green
Arranged by Buddy Skipper

*Rhymes with "how"

If you're feel-in' low-down, Don't know what to do, ___

And you want a show-down, Here's the on-ly dance for you.___ The

D.S.

Hush, Hush

African American Spiritual
Arranged by Don Kalbach

oh, my Lord,__ what shall I do?__
oh, my Lord,__ what shall I do?__

3. You, you, you, Lord, are callin' my name, . . .

Do, Lord

African American Spiritual
Arranged by Georgette LeNorth

Don't Let Your Watch Run Down

Work Song from South Texas
Arranged by Norman Bell

Lively

Don't let your watch run down, Cap-tain, Don't let your watch run down._____ 1. Work-in' on the lev - ee, dol-lar and a half a day, Work-in' on the lev - ee, draw-in' my pay.

D.C. al Fine

2. Workin' on the railroad, mud up to my knees,
Workin' on the railroad, tryin' to please. *Refrain*

3. When you see me comin', hoist your window high,
When you see me leavin', bow down and cry. *Refrain*

Coffee Grows on White Oak Trees

Folk Song from the United States
Arranged by Alan Seale

Flowing
REFRAIN

Cof-fee grows on white oak trees. The riv-er flows with hon-ey-o. Go choose some-one to roam with you, As sweet as m'las - ses can-dy-o.

Fine

VERSE

1. Two in the mid-dle and they can't go o-ver, Two in the mid-dle and they can't go o-ver,

D.C. al Fine

Two in the mid-dle and they can't go o-ver, Hel-lo, Su-san Brown.

2. Swing you another one and you'll get over, *(3 times)* Hello, Susan Brown. *Refrain*

3. Four in the middle and they all go over, *(3 times)* Hello, Susan Brown. *Refrain*

Waltzing with Bears

Words and Music by Dale Marxen
Arranged by Neil Swanson

In Waltz Time

REFRAIN

He goes wa - wa - wa - wa - wa, waltz-ing with bears, Rag - gy bears,

bag - gy bears, shag - gy bears, too. There's noth-ing on earth Un-cle Wal-ter won't

do so he can go waltz-ing, wa - wa - wa - waltz-ing, So

he can go waltz-ing, waltz-ing with bears. *Fine* VERSE 1. I went to his

room in the mid-dle of the night, I tip-toed in - side and turned on the

light, But to my dis-may, he was no-where in sight,

My un-cle Wal-ter goes waltz-ing at night. Now he's

waltz-ing with pand-as, and we don't un-der-stand it, But the

bears all de-mand at least one waltz a day!

2. We bought Uncle Walter a new coat to wear,
   But when he comes home it's all covered with hair,
   And lately I've noticed there are several new tears,
   My uncle Walter goes waltzing with bears. *Refrain*

3. We told Uncle Walter that he should be good,
   And do all the things we say that he should,
   But I know that he'd rather be off in the woods,
   We're afraid we will lose him, we'll lose him for good. *Refrain*

4. We said, "Uncle Walter, oh please won't you stay,"
   And managed to keep him at home for a day,
   But the bears all barged in and they took him away. *(to Coda)*

Railroad Corral

Cowboy Song from the United States
Arranged by Georgette LeNorth

give them full play.
We're up in the morn-ing 'ere break-ing of day, The
Come take up your cin-ches, come shake out your reins, Come

chuck wag - ons bus - y, the flap - jacks in play.
wake your old bron - co and break for the plains.

Now Let Me Fly

African American Spiritual
Arranged by Bruce Simpson

Now let me fly,_____ Now

let me fly,_____ Now let me fly____

way up high,__ Way in the mid-dle of the air.

Don't Let the Wind

Folk Song from St. Helena Island
Arranged by Marilyn J. Patterson

Don't let the wind, don't let the wind, don't let the wind blow

here no more. Oh,_____ don't let the wind, don't let the wind blow here no more.

Erdö, erdö de magos (In the Silent Forest)

English Words by Jean Sinor

Folk Song from Hungary
Arranged by Linda Williams

1. Erd - ö erd - ö de ma - gos a te - te je. Jaj, de ré - gen
1. In the si - lent for - est sings the lone - ly bird, Cold winds blow - ing

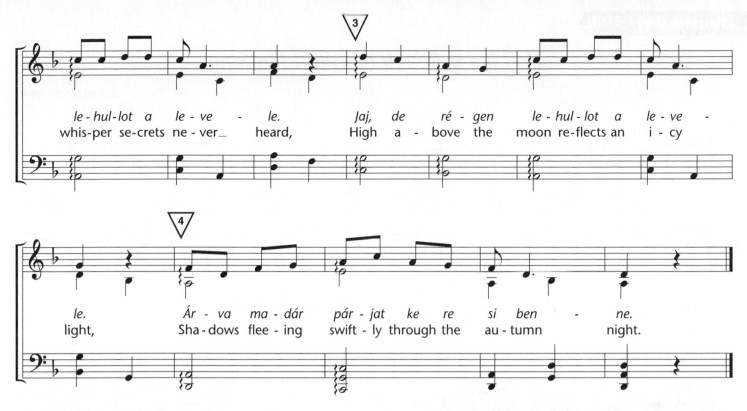

le - hul-lot a le-ve - le. Jaj, de ré-gen le-hul-lot a le-ve -
whis-per se-crets ne-ver___ heard, High a - bove the moon re-flects an i - cy

le. Ár - va ma-dár pár - jat ke re si ben - ne.
light, Sha-dows flee-ing swift - ly through the au - tumn night.

2. Buza kozé szállt a dalos pacsirta,
   Mert odafenn a szemeit kisírta.
   Búzavirág, búzakalász árnyában
   Rágondol a régi, els ö párjára.

2. Through the misty treetop flies the orphaned lark.
   Forest branches creaking stiffly, bare and stark,
   Sadly sounds the plaintive calling high above,
   Calling in the autumn shadows for his love.

Student Page 192

Good Morning

Words and Music by Elizabeth Gilpatrick
Arranged by Anna Leigh

Good morn - ing, good morn - ing, I'm glad you're here to - day. We'll

do our work and have some fun and then go on our way.

I'd Like to Teach the World to Sing

Words and Music by Bill Backer, Billy Davis, Roger Cook, and Roger Greenaway
Arranged by Buddy Skipper

1. I'd like to teach the world to sing____ in
2. like to build the world a home____ and

per - fect har - mo - ny.____ I'd like to hold it
fur - nish it with love.____ Grow ap - ple trees and

in my arms____ and keep it com - pa - ny____ I'd
hon - ey bees____ and snow - white tur - tle doves____

1., 2.   *Fine*

76

3. I'd like to see the world for once
   all standing hand in hand,
   And hear them echo through the hills
   for peace throughout the land.

Turn the Glasses Over

Folk Song from the United States
Arranged by Neil Swanson

With gusto

I've been to Haar-lem, I've been to Do - ver, I've trav-eled this wide world all o - ver,

O - ver, o - ver, three times o - ver, Drink what you have to drink and turn the glass-es o - ver.

Sail - ing east, sail - ing west, Sail - ing o - ver the o - cean,

Bet - ter watch out when the boat be-gins to rock, Or you'll lose your girl in the o - cean.

Hashkediya (Tu b'Shvat *Is Here*)

Words by M. Dushman

Music by M. Ravina
Arranged by Lester Berenbroick

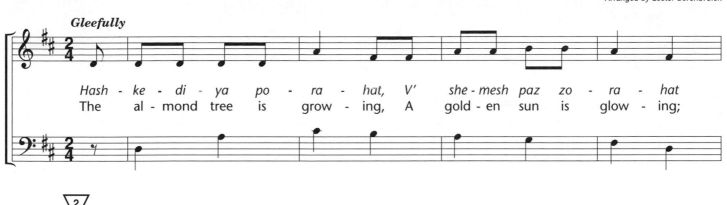

Hash - ke - di - ya po - ra - hat, V' she - mesh paz zo - ra - hat
The al - mond tree is grow - ing, A gold - en sun is glow - ing;

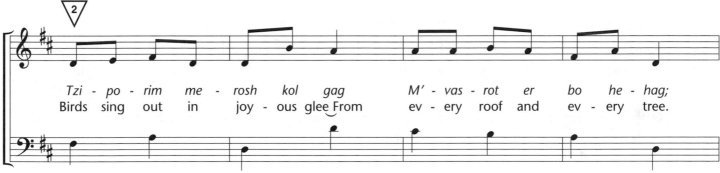

Tzi - po - rim me - rosh kol gag M' - vas - rot er bo he - hag;
Birds sing out in joy - ous glee From ev - ery roof and ev - ery tree.

Tu b' Shvat hi - gi - a Hag ha - i - la - not,
Tu b' Shvat is here, The fes - ti - val of trees.

Tu b' Shvat hi - gi - a Hag ha - i - la - not.
Hail the trees' New Year. Hap - py ho - li - day!

A Ram Sam Sam

Folk Song from Morocco
Arranged by Georgette LeNorth

Not too fast

A ram sam sam, a ram sam sam,

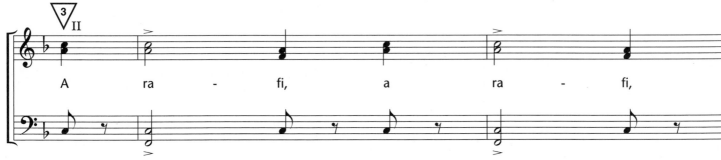

Gu - li gu - li gu - li gu - li gu - li ram sam sam.

A ra - fi, a ra - fi,

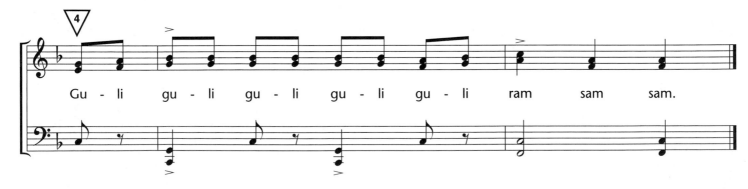

Gu - li gu - li gu - li gu - li gu - li ram sam sam.

Pretty Saro

Folk Song from Kentucky
Arranged by Paul Somers

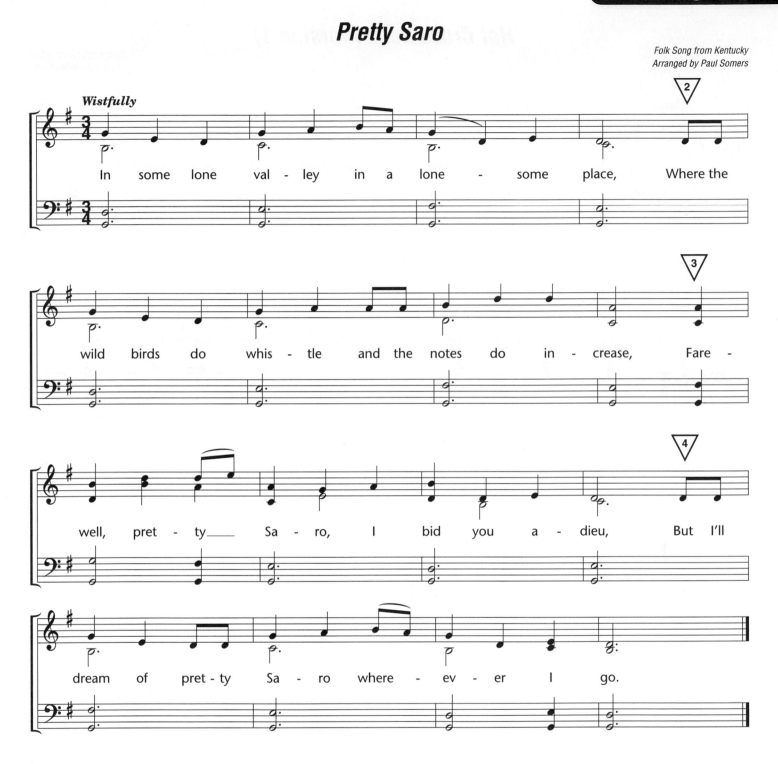

In some lone valley in a lone - some place, Where the

wild birds do whis - tle and the notes do in - crease, Fare -

well, pret - ty___ Sa - ro, I bid you a - dieu, But I'll

dream of pret - ty Sa - ro where - ev - er I go.

Hot Cross Buns (Version 1)

Folk Song from England
Arranged by Wayne Roe

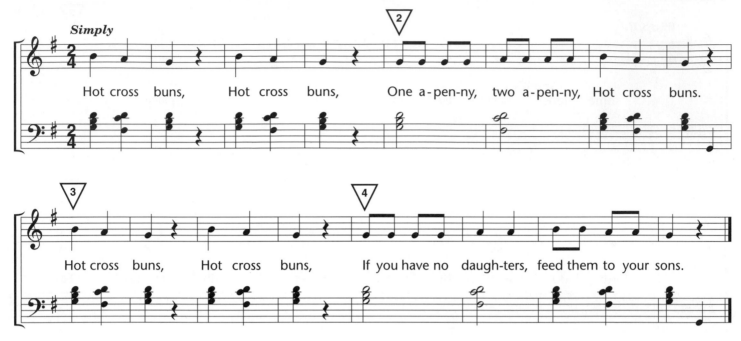

Hot Cross Buns (Version 2)

Folk song from England
Arranged by Lester Berenbroick

A Small Job

Music by Jos Wuytack
Arranged by Marilyn J. Patterson

Playfully

Don't wor-ry if your job is small and your re-wards are few. Re-

mem-ber that the might-y oak was once a nut like you.

Vamos a la mar (Let's Go to the Sea)

Folk Song from Guatemala
Arranged by Rosemary Jacques

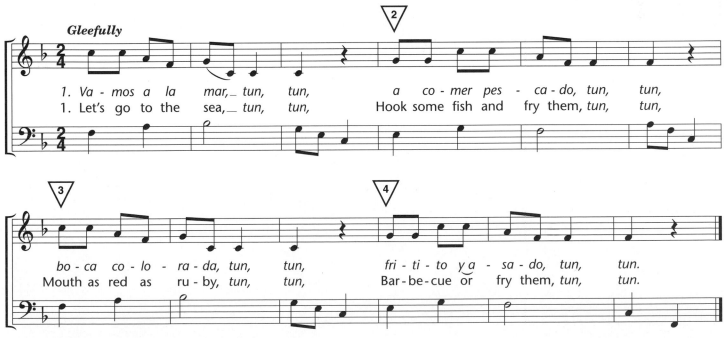

Gleefully

1. Va - mos a la   mar,__ tun,   tun,   a   co - mer pes - ca - do, tun,   tun,
1. Let's go to the   sea,__ tun,   tun,   Hook some fish and   fry them, *tun*,   *tun*,

bo - ca co - lo - ra - da, tun,   tun,   fri - ti - to y a - sa - do, tun,   tun.
Mouth as red as   ru - by, tun,   tun,   Bar-be-cue or   fry them, *tun*,   *tun*.

2. *Vamos a la mar, tun, tun,*
   A comer pescado, tun, tun
   fritito y asado, tun, tun,
   en sartén de palo, tun, tun,

2. Let's go to the sea, *tun, tun,*
   Catch a fish and grill it, *tun, tun,*
   Barbecue or fry it, *tun, tun,*
   In a wooden skillet, *tun, tun.*

Sweet Potatoes

Creole Folk Song
Arranged by Don Kalbach

Animated

1. Soon as we all cook sweet po-ta-toes, Sweet po-ta-toes,
2. Soon as sup-per's done, Ma-ma hol-lers, Ma-ma hol-lers,

Sweet po-ta-toes, Soon as we all
Ma-ma hol-lers, Soon as sup-per's

cook sweet po-ta-toes, Eat 'em right straight up!
done, Ma-ma hol-lers, "Get a-long to bed!"

3. Soon's we touch our heads to the pillow,...
   Go to sleep right smart!

4. Soon's the rooster crow in the mornin',...
   Gotta wash our face!

He's Got the Whole World in His Hands

African American Spiritual
Arranged by Don Kalbach

2. He's got the wind and the rain in his hands, *(3 times)*
   He's got the whole world in his hands.

3. He's got-a you and me, brother, in his hands,
   He's got-a you and me, sister, in his hands,
   He's got-a you and me, brother, in his hands,
   He's got the whole world in his hands.

Sing, America, Sing!

Words and Music by Jill Gallina

Sing, A-mer - i - ca, sing! Lift up your voice__ in a song.

Sing, A-mer - i - ca, sing! Sing with a voice__ proud and

strong. With man - y fac - es from man - y plac - es, A

joy - ful mes - sage we bring, a cel - e - bra - tion a -

cross our na - tion, Let mer - ry mu - sic ring!

Sing, A-mer - i - ca, sing! Lift up your voice_ in a

song. Sing, A-mer - i - ca, sing! Sing with a voice_ proud and

strong. With songs we greet_ you, as now we treat_ you to a world of mel - o -

dies,   So,   lift up your voice___ in a   song,   and

soon   all A - mer - i - ca,   Will   sing a - long.

(Note: Recording includes 17 additional measures.)

Sing,   A - mer - i - ca,   sing,   A - mer - i - ca,   sing!

Bling Blang *The accompaniment for this song is found on p. 92.*

I've Been Working on the Railroad

Work Song from the United States
Arranged by Lucy Snell

Bling Blang

Words and Music by Woody Guthrie
Arranged by Merle Buford

Jaunty

1. You get a ham-mer and I'll get a nail; You catch a bird and I'll catch a snail;
2. I'll grab some mud and you grab some clay So when it rains it won't wash a-way.

You bring a board and I'll bring a saw, and we'll build a house for the ba - by - o.
We'll build a house that'll be so strong, The winds will sing my baby a song.

REFRAIN
Bling blang, ham-mer with my ham-mer, Zing - o zang-o, cut-ting with my saw.

Song of the Fishes

Sea Shanty from the United States
Arranged by Carol Jay

1. Come all you bold fish - er - men, lis - ten to me, I'll sing you a
2. First comes the blue - fish a wag - ging his tail, He comes up on

song of the fish in the sea. Then blow ye winds west - er - ly,
deck and yells, "All hands make sail!"

west - er - ly blow, We're bound to the south-ward, so stead - y we go.

3. Next come the herrings, with their little tails,
   They man sheets and halyards and set all the sails.

4. Next comes the porpoise, with his short snout,
   He jumps on the bridge and yells, "Ready, about!"

5. Then comes the mackerel, with his striped back,
   He flopped on the bridge and yelled, "Board the main tack!"

6. Up jumps the fisherman, stalwart and grim,
   And with his big net he scooped them all in.

Peace Like a River

African American Spiritual
Arranged by Lawrence Elsman

1. I've got peace like a riv-er, I've got peace like a riv-er, I've got
2. I've got joy like a foun-tain, I've got joy like a foun-tain, I've got
3. I've got love like the o-cean, I've got love like the o-cean, I've got

peace like a riv-er in my soul. I've got peace like a
joy like a foun-tain in my soul. I've got joy like a
love like the o-cean in my soul. I've got love like the

riv - er, I've got peace like a riv - er, I've got peace like a
foun-tain, I've got joy like a foun-tain, I've got joy like a
o-cean, I've got love like the o-cean, I've got love like the

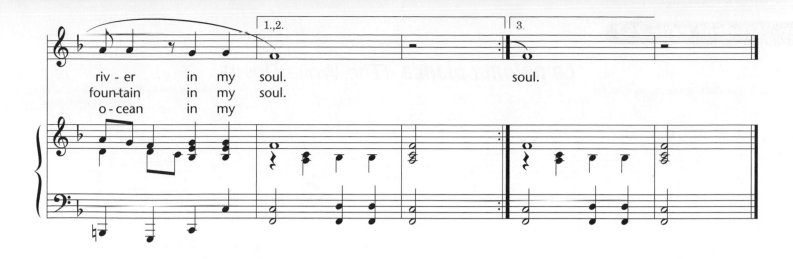

Texas Cowboy

Folk Song from Texas
Arranged by Edward F. Corson

95

La paloma blanca (The White Dove)

English Words by Ruth De Cesare (adapted)

Folk Song from the Southwestern United States
Arranged by Alice Firgau

With tenderness

1

Yo soy tu pa - lo - ma blan - ca,
I'm your white dove, hear me sing - ing;

2

tú e - res mi pi - chón a - zul,
You're my pret - ty pi - geon blue.

3

a - mí - ma - me tus plu - mi - tas,
Turn your beak to me, my dear one,

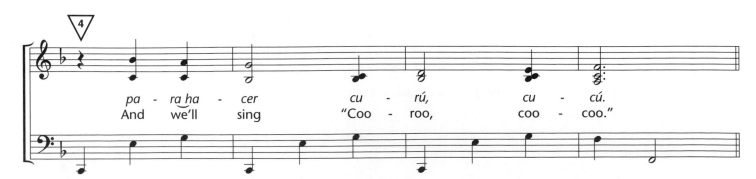

4

pa - ra ha - cer cu - rú, cu - cú.
And we'll sing "Coo - roo, coo - coo."

A la jo - ta, jo - ta que bai - le, bo - ni - to,
To the jo - ta, jo - ta the fair____ one danc - es,

A la jo - ta, jo - ta que bai - le él so - li - to,
To the jo - ta, jo - ta the fair____ one danc - es,

A la jo - ta, jo - ta y con buen mo - di - to,
To the jo - ta, jo - ta the fair____ one danc - es,

pa - ra ha cer cu - rú, cu - cú.
"Coo - roo, coo - roo, coo - coo."

Nani wale na hala *(Lovely Hala Trees)*

English Words by Alice Firgau

Folk Song from Hawaii
Arranged by Don Kalbach

Na - ni wa - le na____ ha - la,   E - a,   e - a.   O   Na - u - e
Love - ly are   the   ha - la   trees,____   E - a,   e - a.   Sway - ing   by   the

i - ke ka - i   E - a,   e - a.   Ke____ o - ni   a____ e - la
gen - tle seas.____   E - a,   e - a.   Near Ha - e - na   ha - las   grow,____

E - a,   e - a.   Pi - li ma - i   Ha - e - na   E - a,   e - a.
E - a,   e - a.   In   Na - u - e   breez - es   blow.____   E - a,   e - a

98

Take Me Out to the Ball Game

Words by Jack Norworth

Music by Albert von Tilzer
Arranged by Eleanor Aiken

You're a Grand Old Flag

Words and Music by George M. Cohan
Arranged by Donald Scafuri

It's a Small World

Words and Music by Richard M. Sherman and Robert B. Sherman
Arranged by David Fiorenza

101

Al tambor (The Drum Song)

English Words by Mary Shamrock

Children's Song from Panama
Arranged by Antonio de la Campa

Lightly

Al tam - bor, al tam - bor, al tam - bor de la a - le -
Won't you play, won't you play, won't you play the tam - bor -

grí - a. Yo quie - ro que tú me lle - ves al tam - bor de la a - le -
ci - to? In time with the tam - bor - ci - to we en - joy our life to -

Fine

grí - a. Ma - rí - a, oh Ma - rí - a, Ma - rí - a, a - mi - ga
geth - er. Ma - ri - a, oh, Ma - ri - a, this drum is a spe - cial

D.C. al Fine

mí - a, Yo quie - ro que tú me lle - ves al tam - bor de la a - le - grí - a.
trea - sure. In time with the tam - bor - ci - to we en - joy our life to - geth - er.

102

Karangatia ra

Collected by Michael Hamblin

Maori Action Song from New Zealand
Arranged by Georgette LeNorth

Sarika keo *(Bird Song)*

English Words by David Eddleman

Folk Song from Cambodia
Arranged by Ting Ho

Tenderly

1. Sa - ri - ka   keo   euy   si____ ey   kang____
1. Oh,____ ti - ny   bird,   tell   me   what   do   you

kang? Ey sa - ri - yaing. Sa - ri - ka keo euy si____ ey kang____
eat? Ah sa - ri - yang. Oh,____ ti - ny bird, tell me what do you

kang? Ey sa - ri - yaing. Si phle dam - bang pra - choeuk____ knea____
eat? Ah sa - ri - yang. A cac - tus fruit so ripe____ and____

leng. Euy keo keo____ euy, euy keo keo____ euy.____
sweet. Oy koy koy____ oy, oy koy koy____ oy.____

2. *Slap vea chakk kbach*
    moat vea thveu phleng.
    Ey sariyainng.
    (Repeat)
    Prachoeuk knea leng
    leu mek proeuksa.
    Euy keo keo euy,
    euy keo keo euy.

2. High in the sky
    you dance on the wing.
    Ah sariyang.
    (Repeat)
    High on a branch you fuss at everything!
    Oy koy koy oy,
    oy koy koy oy.

Shu ha mo (Frogs)

English Words by Betty Warner Dietz
and Thomas Choonbai Park

Folk Song from China
Arranged by Hui Chung

Yi zhi hu ma yi zhang zui
Each frog has a sin - gle mouth,

liang zhi yan jing si tiao tui
He has two eyes and four legs.

Pin pong pin pong tiao xia____ shui ya
Ping pong, ping pong, count them_ with me.

ha ma bu chi shui
Dur - ing time of peace,

tai ping___ nian
frogs do not drink.

he er mei zi xi
Wa - ter lil - ies float

shui shang piao.
on the pond.

Pust' 'vsegda budet sonse (May the Sun Shine Forever)

Russian Words by L. Oshanin
English Words by Alice Firgau

Music by A. Ostrovsky
Arranged by Alan Seale

Pust' 'vse-gda bu-det son-se, Pust' 'vse-
May the sun shine for-ev-er, May blue

gda bu-det nye-ba, Pust' 'vse-gda bu-det
skies be for-ev-er, May there ev-er be

ma-ma, Pust' 'vse-gda bu-do ya! gda bu-do ya!
Ma-ma, May there ev-er be me! ev-er be me!

Mübärak *(Happy Birthday)*

English Words by Mary Shamrock

Persian Birthday Song
As sung by Hooshang Bagheri
Arranged by Audrey Schultz

Mü - bär - ak, mü-bär - ak, ta-val - lu-det mü-bä - rak, mü-bä -
Hap-py day, hap-py day, here it is, your hap-py day. Hap-py

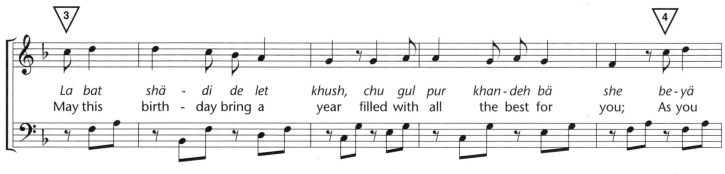

rak, mü - bä - rak ta-val lu-det mü-bä - rak.
day, hap-py day, here it is, your hap-py day.

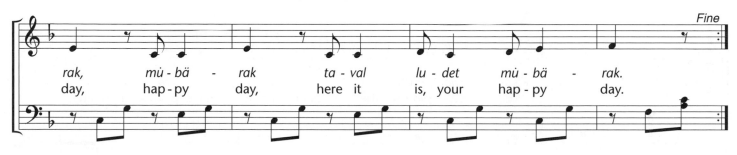

La bat shä - di de let khush, chu gul pur khan-deh bä she be-yä
May this birth - day bring a year filled with all the best for you; As you

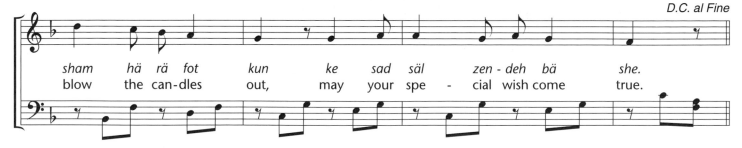

sham hä rä fot kun ke sad säl zen-deh bä she.
blow the can-dles out, may your spe - cial wish come true.

107

Artsa alinu (Come to the Land)

Folk Song from Israel
Arranged by Mary Jean Nelson

With a strong rhythm

Ar - sta a - li - nu, ar - tsa a - li - nu, ar - tsa a - li -
Come to the land with joy and with spir - it, Come to our na - tive

nu. K'var cha - rash - nu v' - gam za - ra - nu.
land. We have plowed the fields and have plant - ed grain.

A - val od lo ka - tsar - nu. A - val od lo ka - tsar - nu.
We'll reap a might - y har - vest. We'll reap a might - y har - vest.

Sansaw akroma

Game Song from Ghana
Arranged by Alice Firgau

St. Patrick Was a Gentleman

Folk Song from Ireland
Arranged by Martha Hilley

Lively

St. Pat - rick was a gen - tle - man, He came of de - cent peo - ple, In

Dub - lin town he built a church, And on it put a stee - ple. His

1. fa - ther was a Call - a - ghan, His mo - ther was a Bra - dy, His
aunt was an O - 'Shaugh - ness - y, And his un - cle was a

2. Gra - dy. **REFRAIN** Then suc - cess to bold St. Pat - rick's fist, He was a saint so clev - er, He

gave the snakes and toads a twist, And ban - ished them for - ev - er.

Bonavist' Harbour

Folk Song fom Newfoundland
Arranged by Lester Berenbroick

1. Oh, there's lots of fish in Bon-a-vist' Har-bour, Lots of fish right
2. Well, now, Un-cle George got up in the morn-ing He got up in a

in a-round here. Boys and girls are fish-ing to-geth-er, For-ty five miles from
won-der-ful tear. Ripped the seat right out of his britch-es Now he's got ne'er

REFRAIN

Car - bon-ear. Oh, catch a-hold this one, catch a-hold that one,
pair to wear.

Swing a-round this one, swing a-round she. Dance a-round this one,

dance a-round that one, Did-dle dum this one, did-dle dum dee.

111

Sierra Morena

English Words by Cory Reeves

Folk Song from Mexico
Arranged by Joyce Kalbach

De Sie - rra Mo - re - na que vien - en ha -
The gen - tle - man brings them from Sie - rra Mo -

jan - do cuat - ro pa - lo - mi - tas y un vie - jo a - rri - an - do.
re - na, four___ white___ doves sing - ing beau - ti - ful songs.___

La calle ancha *(The Wide Street)*

English Words by Mary Shamrock

Folk Song from Puerto Rico
Arranged by Alice Firgau

Steadily

La ca - lle an - cha, cha, cha de San Ber -
A - long the street wide, wide, wide called San Ber -

nar - do, do, do Tie - ne u - na fuen - te, te,
nar - do, do, do There is a foun - tain, tain,

te con cua - tro ca - ños, ños, ños.
tain from which four streams flow, flow, flow.

2. *Los cuatro caños, ños, ños*
dan agua hermosa, sa, sa
Para los niños, ños, ños
de Zaragoza, za, za.

2. In Zaragoza, za, za
They shine and sparkle, kle, kle
For all the children, dren, dren
A gift so simple, ple, ple.

113

Poco, Le' Me 'Lone

Folk Song from Tobago
Arranged by Marilyn J. Patterson

Jan ken pon

English Words by Mary Shamrock

Collected by Mary Shamrock at the
Nishi Hongwanji Temple Dharma School
Arranged by Joyce Kalbach

With good cheer

O - na - ka ga su - i - ta - ra goo goo goo,
When you have a hair - cut, scis - sors snip, snip, snip.

Ka - mi - no - ke no - bi ta - ra cho - ki cho - ki cho - ki,
Hun - gry stom - achs of - ten make a grum - ble, grum - ble, grum - ble.

Ho - ko - ri wo ha - ta - i - te pa pa pa,
Wip - ing with a dust rag makes a slap, slap, slap.

(Spoken)

Jan ken pon do goo cho - ki pa. Jan ken pon!
Snip, grumble, slap, now show me your hand! Jan ken pon!

Four White Horses

Folk Song from the Caribbean
Arranged by John Detroy

Four white hors - es on the riv - er, Hey, hey,__ hey,__ up to - mor - row,

Up to - mor - row is a rain - y day. Come on up__ to the shal - low bay.

Shal - low bay__ is a ripe ba - na - na. Up to - mor - row is a rain - y day.

Ah, eu entrei na roda *(I Came to Try This Game)*

Circle Game from Brazil
Arranged by Pira Almeida

Lightly

Ah, eu en - trei na ro - da, pa - ra ver co - mo se -
I came to try this game.___ I came to see the peo - ple

dan - ça, Ah, eu en - trei na con - tra dan - ça, Ah, eu nao sei dan -
danc - ing. I came here to join the fun, but don't know how to

çar! La' vai uma, la', váo du - ás, la' váo três, pe - la ter -
dance! There goes one and there goes two, there goes three, and on the

cei - ra, la' se vai o meu a - mor de va - por p'ra ca - choi - e - ra!
third, There goes my sweet - heart on a steam - boat down the riv - er to the sea.

117

Little Johnny Brown

African American Singing Game
Arranged by Lester Berenbroick

Nie chcę cię znác *(Don't Want to Know You)*

English Words by Mary Shamrock

Folk Song from Poland
Arranged by Martha Hilley

I Wonder Where Maria's Gone

Folk Song from Kentucky
Arranged by Carol Jay

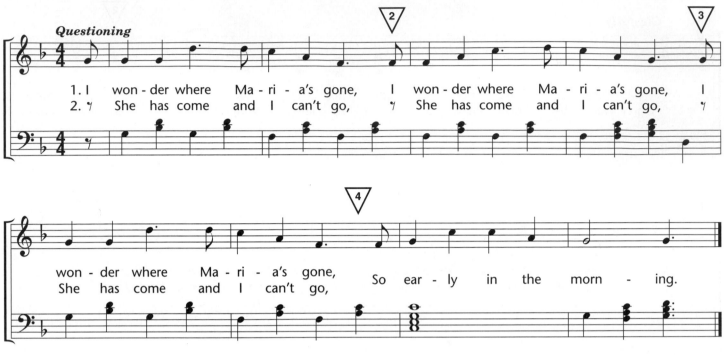

Questioning

1. I wonder where Maria's gone, I wonder where Maria's gone, I
2. She has come and I can't go, She has come and I can't go,

wonder where Maria's gone, So early in the morning.
She has come and I can't go,

3. Yonder she comes and "How do you do?"
Yonder she comes and "How do you do?"
Yonder she comes and "How do you do?"
So early in the morning.

4. Shake her hand and wave on through,
Shake her hand and wave on through,
Shake her hand and wave on through,
So early in the morning.

Al citrón

Latino Nonsense Song from California
Arranged by Neil Swanson

With Bounce

Al ci - trón de un fan - dan - go, San - go, San - go, Sa - ba -

ré. Sa - ba - ré de la ron - de - lla Con su tri - ki, tri - ki - trón.

Al ánimo

English Words by Alice Firgau

Folk Song from Spain
Arranged by Cameron McGraw

2. Al ánimo, al ánimo,
   ¿con qué se hace el dinero?
   Al ánimo, al ánimo,
   con cáscara de huevo.

2. Al ánimo, al ánimo,
   From what is money made?
   Al ánimo, al ánimo,
   From cotton thread and braid.

Big Beautiful Planet

Words and Music by Raffi

Moderately, with feeling

REFRAIN

There's a big beau-ti-ful plan-et in the sky,_____ And it's my home,_____ It's where I

live. You and man-y oth-ers live here too._____ The earth is our home,_____ It's where we

live._____

Fine VERSE

1. We can feel the pow-er of the noon-day sun, A
2. We can feel the spir-it of a blow-ing wind, A

blaz-ing ball of fire___ up a - bove; Shin-ing light and warmth e-nough for
might-y source of pow-er in our lives. Of - fer - ing an - oth - er way to

D.C. al Fine

ev - ery - one, A gift to ev - ery na - tion from a star.
fill our needs, Na-ture's gift to help us car - ry on.

El mes de abril *(The Month of April)*

Folk Song from Spain
Arranged by Anita P. Davis

Happily

I

El   mes   de a - bril   lle - gó,   y el   cu - cu   ya   can -
The   month   of   A - pril's   here,   The   cuck - oo's   song   we

II

tó: Cu - cú,   cu - cú   el   cu - cu   ya   can - tó.
hear.   Cuck - oo,   cuck - oo,   the   cuck - oo's   song   we   hear.

Hama chi dori (Plovers)

The accompaniment for this song appears on p. 126.

Bluebonnets of Texas

Words and Music by Beatrice P. Krone
Arranged by Bernie Anderson, Jr.

With feeling

1. Blue - bon - nets of Tex - as, they bloom in the spring. A
2. Though far o'er the wide world a - roam - ing I go, I'll

car - pet of blue that will make your heart sing. I
dream of the land where the blue - bon - nets grow. Though

Hama chi dori (Plovers)

Words by Meishu Kashima

School Song from Japan
Music by Ryutaro Hirota
Arranged by Leslie Jefferson

Quietly

Aa   o   ii   tsu   ki   yo
When   the   blue___   moon -

no   ha   ma   be___   ni   wa___   oh   ya   wo   sa
light   shines   up - on___   the   shore,___   From   a - mong   the

ga   shi   te   na___   ku   to   ri   ga___   Na   mi
gleam - ing   waves   ba - by   plov - ers   soar,___   Look - ing

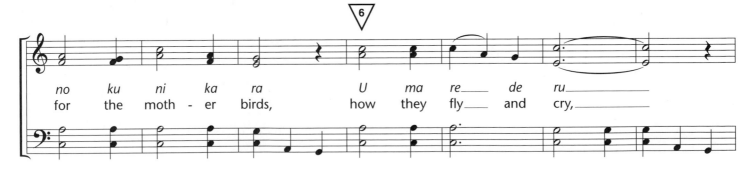

no   ku   ni   ka   ra   U   ma   re___   de   ru___
for   the   moth - er   birds,   how   they   fly___   and   cry,___

Nu   re   ta   tsu   ba   sa   no   ghi - n   no   i   ro.___
Wa - ter   bathed,___   bright___   wings,   sil - ver - y   the   sky.___

126

El sapito (The Little Toad)

Words by Jose Sebastian Tallón
English Words courtesy of CP Language Institute

Music by Wilbur Alpírez Quesada
Arranged by Martha Hilley

Questioningly

Na - die sa - be don - de vi - ve, en la ca - sa no lo vió,
No one knows just where the toad lives. We can't find him in the house.

pe - ro to - dos lo es - cu - cha - mos, el sa - pi - to glo, glo, glo.
But we know we all can hear it. Lit - tle toad, sing glo, glo, glo.

Vi - vi - rá en la chi - me - ne - a? Vi - ve o - cul - to en u - na flor?
May - be liv - ing in the chim - ney, May - be hid - den in a rose.

Don - de can - ta cuan - do llue - ve? El sa - pi - to glo.
When it rains where does the toad sing? Lit - tle toad, sing glo.

127

It's a Beautiful Day

Words and Music by Greg Scelsa
Arranged by Mary Jean Nelson

See the sun shin-ing in the win-dow, time to start a new day. Can't you hear the song-birds sing-in'? Got-ta sing out loud and say / Yes it's a That it's a beau-ti-ful day for run-nin' in the sun, a beau-ti-ful day that's just be-gun, a beau-ti-ful day to do what I wan-na do,

Look Out for Mother Earth

Words and Music by Bryan Louiselle
Arranged by Christopher Hatcher

With a strong rhythm

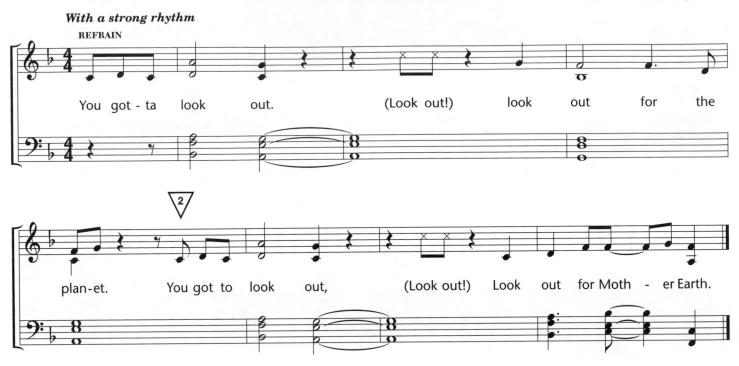

REFRAIN

You got-ta look out. (Look out!) look out for the

plan-et. You got to look out, (Look out!) Look out for Moth - er Earth.

VERSES

1. We gotta tell you, Mom,
   we gotta tell you, Dad.
   That we don't have
   ev'rything you had.
   We're not talkin' money
   or a life of ease;
   We're talkin' water, (Clean water!)
   clean water and trees.
   Hey, what's up with all the smoke
   from the factories?
   (to Refrain)

2. There's stuff goin' on
   that you can't even see:
   There's a hole in the sky
   where a hole shouldn't be.
   We're talking ozone. (Ozone?) Definitely.
   And if we don't cut back on C. F. C.s,
   We're gonna all need sunblock
   a thousand and three.
   (to Refrain)

3. Ev'ry fish and mammal,
   ev'ry insect and bird
   Makes a contribution,
   is a voice to be heard.
   Won't you hear the voice?
   Won't you feel the pain?
   They're sayin' oil spills!
   (Oil spills?) and acid rain.
   And everything else we're puttin'
   down the drain! Here we go again!
   (to Refrain)

4. Hey, teacher,
   won't you help us plot a strategy?
   Plan a plan for the planet.
   Plant a flower or tree.
   Promote ecological diversity.
   Not just for you, not just for me.
   It's for the kids
   in the next (Next!) century.
   (to Refrain)

This page purposely left blank to facilitate page turns.

The World We Love

Words and Music by Raffi and Michael Creber
Arranged by Anita P. Davis

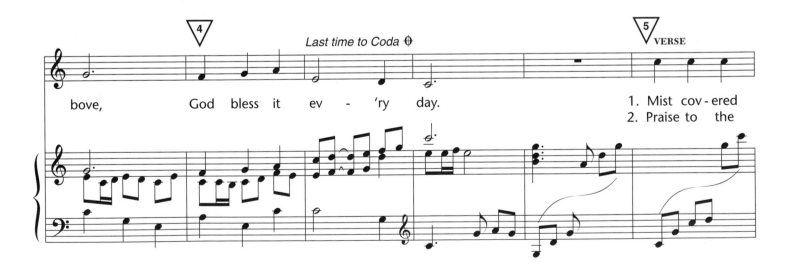

moun-tains that wel-come the sun,
far-mer out work-in' the fields,

Buds on the branch-es,
Seed-ling to har-vest,

morn-ings be-
food for our

gun,
meals,

Dew-drops and blue-birds just start-ing to sing
Ma-mas and pa-pas and hearts filled with love

Praise for the
for each and

⊕ Coda

brand new day.
ev - 'ry day.

day.

poco ritardando

3. Here's to the rivers that run wild and free.
The pull of the tides, the rush of the sea,
Gold crimson sunsets to color our dreams,
In each and ev'ry day. *Refrain*

A Song of One

Words and Music by John Forster and Tom Chapin
Arranged by Jill Gallina

Sing a song of one, One for the yel - low sun, the yel - low sun that's shin - ing down on ev - 'ry - one

2. Sing a song of two, two for the sky of blue, *(to verse 2 ending)*
3. Sing a song of three, three for the red - wood tree, *(to verse 3 ending)*
4. Sing a song of four, four for the sand - y shore, *(to verse 4 ending)*
5. Sing a song of five, five for the things a - live, *(to verse 5 ending)*

Sing Your Story

Words and Music by Bryan Louiselle
Arranged by Buddy Skipper

Don Gato

English Words by Margaret Marks

Folk Song from Mexico
Arranged by Alice Firgau

2. Con una gatita blanca,
   sobrina de un gato pardo,
   que no la había más linda,. . .
   que no la había más linda, . . .
   en las casas de aquel barrio.

3. Don Gato con la alegría,
   se ha caído del tejado;
   ha roto siete costillas, . . .
   ha roto siete costillas, . . .
   las dos orejas y el rabo.

4. A visitarlo venían,
   médicos y cirujanos;
   todos dicen que se muere, . . .
   todos dicen que se muere, . . .
   que don Gato está muy malo.

5. El gatito ya se ha muerto,
   ya se ha muerto el buen don Gato;
   a enterrar ya se lo llevan, . . .
   a enterrar ya se lo llevan, . . .
   todos los gatos llorando.

2. "I adore you!" wrote the lady cat,
   Who was fluffy, white, and nice and fat.
   There was not a sweeter kitty, . . .
   In the country or the city, . . .
   And she said she'd wed Don Gato!

3. Oh, Don Gato jumped so happily,
   He fell off the roof and broke his knee,
   Broke his ribs and all his whiskers, . . .
   And his little solar plexus, . . .
   "¡Ay caramba!" cried Don Gato!

4. Then the doctors all came on the run
   Just to see if something could be done,
   And they held a consultation, . . .
   About how to save their patient, . . .
   How to save Señor Don Gato!

5. But in spite of ev'rything they tried,
   Poor Señor Don Gato up and died,
   Oh, it wasn't very merry, . . .
   Going to the cemetery, . . .
   For the ending of Don Gato!

6. Cuando pasaba el entierro,
   por la plaza del pescado,
   al olor de las sardinas, . . .
   al olor de las sardinas, . . .
   don Gato ha resucitado.

6. When the funeral passed the market square,
   Such a smell of fish was in the air,
   Though his burial was slated, . . .
   He became re-animated! . . .
   He came back to life, Don Gato!

Student Page 354

If a Tiger Calls

Words and Music by Elizabeth Gilpatrick
Arranged by Ivan Karadinsky

1. If a ti - ger calls in the mid - dle of the night and in -
2. If a li - on calls in the mid - dle of the day and in -
3. If a croco - dile calls and in - vites you out to dine, tell him,

vites you out for a lit - tle ev' - ning bite, do be war - y, for zo -
vites you out for an af - ter - noon buf - fet, do be war - y, for zo -
"Thank you, next De - cem - ber would be fine." And be war - y, for zo -

Last verse to Coda

ol - o - gists have shown that the ti - ger lies on the phone.
ol - o - gists have shown that the li - on lies on the phone.
ol - o - gists will state that the

Coda

croc-o-dile lies, the croc-o-dile lies, the croc-o-dile lies in wait!

139

El barquito (The Tiny Boat)

English Words by Kim Williams

Folk Song from Latin America
Arranged by Joyce Kalbach

Rhythmically

Ha - bí a u - na vez un bar - co chi - qui - ti - co,
Oh, there was once a boat so ve - ry ti - ny,

Ha - bí a u - na vez un bar - co chi - qui - ti - co,
Oh, there was once a boat so ve - ry ti - ny,

Ha - bí a u - na vez un bar - co chi - qui - ti - co, Que no po -
Oh, there was once a boat so ve - ry ti - ny, So ve - ry

dí - a, que no po - dí - a, que no po - dí - a na - ve - gar. Pa - sa - ron
ti - ny, so ve - ry ti - ny, it could not e - ven sail a - way. It sat for

El rabel (The Violin)

English Words by Patricia Shehan Campbell

Folk Song from Chile
Arranged by Carol Jay

El ra - bel pa - ra ser fi - no ha de ser de ver - de
The ra - bel it is so fine and it's made of fresh green

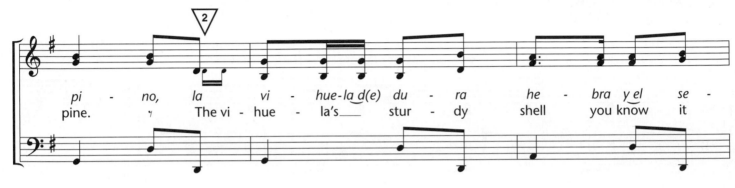

pi - no, la vi - hue-la d(e) du - ra he - bra y el se -
pine. The vi - hue - la's____ stur - dy shell you know it

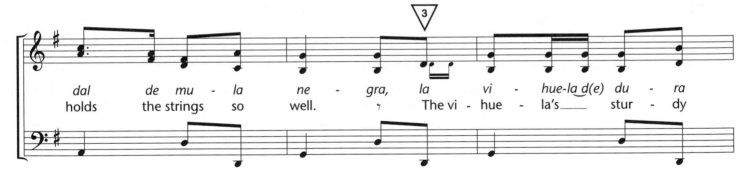

dal de mu - la ne - gra, la vi - hue-la d(e) du - ra
holds the strings so well. The vi - hue - la's____ stur - dy

Fine

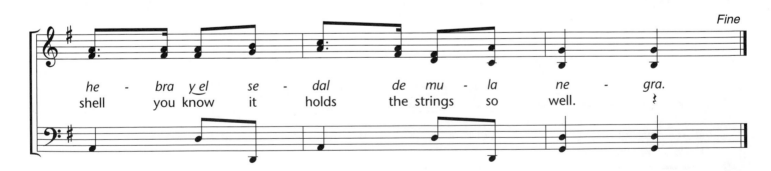

he - bra y el se - dal de mu - la ne - gra.
shell you know it holds the strings so well.

An - da mo - re - ni - ta re - co - je e - se pa - nue - lo.
Let the girl___ go there and pick up the hand - ker - chief.

Mi - ra que es de se - da y Lo a - rras - tras por el sue - lo.
Silk - en hand - ker - chief: she's drag - ging it on the floor.

We've Got Lots in Common
from *Charlotte's Web*

Words and Music by Richard M. Sherman and Robert B. Sherman
Arranged by Don Kalbach

REFRAIN

1. Oh, we've got
2., 3. 'Cause we've got lots in com - mon where it
4. We've all got

real - ly counts, Where it real - ly counts, we've got large a -

mounts. What we look like does-n't count an ounce, We've got lots in

Rockin' Robin

Words and Music by Leon René
Arranged by Don Kalbach

146

Fine

A pret-ty lit-tle ra-ven at the bird band-stand

Taught him how to do the bop and it was grand. They start-ed go-in' stead-y, and

D.S. al Fine

bless my soul, He out-bopped the buz-zard and the o - ri-ole.

Wooly Bully

Words and Music by Domingo Samudio
Arranged by Edward F. Corson and Don Kalbach

2. Hatty told Matty
   Let's don't take no chance,
   Let's not be L 7
   Come and learn to dance
   Refrain

3. Matty told Hatty
   That's the thing to do,
   Get yo' someone really
   To pull the wool with you–
   Refrain

Let's Celebrate

Words and Music by Jill Gallina
Arranged by Leslie Jefferson

Bright

1.,3. We're gon - na have a cel - e - bra - tion.
2. Oh, how we all love cel - e - bra - tions

Oh, won't you join us, ev - 'ry - one?___
And spread - ing joy a - cross the land.___

Our hearts are filled with such e - la - tion. We'll dance and sing and
So tell your friends and your re - la - tions. It's time for us to

3rd time to Coda

have such fun.___
all join hands.___ As our voi - ces___ ring,

151

Go With the Music and Sing

Words and Music by Rhonda Macken
Arranged by Joyce Kalbach

Some to sing_ by day and some by night, So go with the mu - sic and sing._

Go with the mu-sic and sing.__ Let's sing!__

Hevenu shalom aleichem (We Come to Greet You in Peace)

Hebrew Folk Song
Arranged by Avram Stem

In the Pumpkin Patch

Words and Music by Elizabeth Gilpatrick
Arranged by Jill Gallina

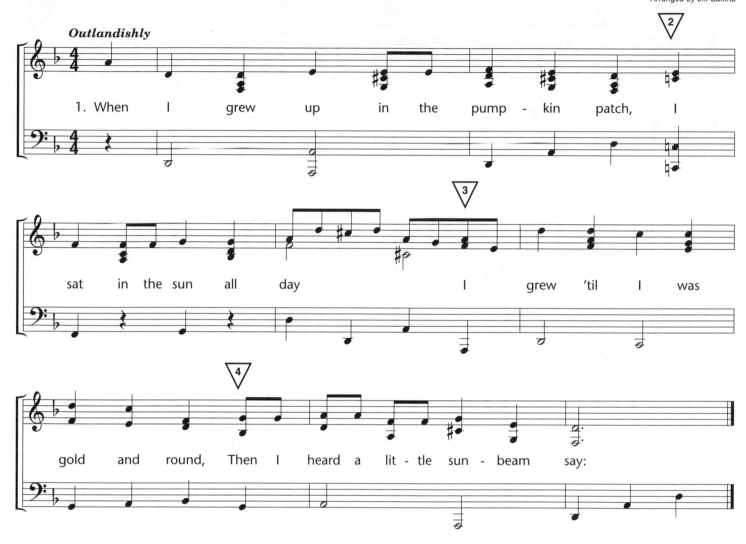

2. "Roll around, little pumpkin in the pumpkin patch,
Oh, tumble and turn and sway.
Roll around in the grasses and the weeds and the thatch,
Oh, spin and roll and play.

3. "But when the sun is sinking low
And shadows steal the light,
Hurry back to your home in the garden row;
Curl up in your vines so tight."

Halloween Is a Very Unusual Night

Words and Music by Ned Ginsburg

How could an-y-bo-dy sleep? And the

mon-sters march, while the witch-es take flight. Yes,

Hal-lo-ween is a ver-y un-u-su-al night!

sfz Yes, Hal-lo-ween is a ver-y un-u-su-al

night! *sfz* *sfz*

Over the River and Through the Wood

Words by Lydia Maria Child

Traditional
Arranged by Georgette LeNorth

Knock No More

Words and Music by Elizabeth Gilpatrick
Arranged by Marilyn J. Patterson

When Old Man Win-ter___ comes knock-ing at your door, he'll

nip your fin-gers___ and freeze you to the core.

Knock! Knock! Can't come in! Knock no more!

Chanukah Games

Words by Rose C. Engel and Judith M. Berman

Music by Judith M. Berman
Arranged by Don Kalbach

With good cheer

VERSE

1. Cha - nu-kah's the time for games. Read - y, now be - gin!
2. Round and round the drey - dl goes, See it hop and run.

Spin your drey - dl, let it go, Ev - 'ry-one join in.
When at last it stops on *nun,* Priz - es? Not a one.

Spin your drey - dl, let it go, Ev - 'ry-one join in!
When at last it stops on *nun,* Priz - es? Not a one.

REFRAIN

Nun and *gi - mel, hay* and *shin,* Los - er, win-ner, spin and spin!

1.

2. spin and spin!

3. In a circle, dreydl, turn,
   turn and slowly sway.
   If you stop on *gimel* now,
   I win all—Hooray!
   If you stop on *gimel* now,
   I win all—Hooray! *Refrain*

4. Funny little dreydl top,
   how you make me laugh!
   But if now you stop on *hay.*
   I take only half!
   But if now you stop on *hay,*
   I take only half! *Refrain*

5. Whirling, twirling, dreydl, go,
   on one foot you dance;
   Shin says I must put one in
   and take another chance!
   Shin says I must put one in
   and take another chance! *Refrain*

Hanuka, Hanuka

Words and Music by Flory Jagoda
Arranged by Leslie Jefferson

2. *Hanuka, Hanuka,*
Ocho diyas de kantar.
Hanuka, Hanuka,
Ocho diyas de kantar.
Refrain

3. *Hanuka, Hanuka,*
Ocho diyas de bayar.
Hanuka, Hanuka,
Ocho diyas de bayar.
Refrain

4. *Hanuka, Hanuka,*
Ocho diyas de guzar.
Hanuka, Hanuka,
Ocho diyas de guzar.
Refrain

2. Hanuka, Hanuka,
Eight days of singing for Hanuka.
Everyone sing, let voices ring,
Eight days of singing for Hanuka.
Refrain

3. Hanuka, Hanuka,
Eight days of dancing for Hanuka.
Raise arms high, let feet fly,
Eight days of dancing for Hanuka.
Refrain

4. Hanuka, Hanuka,
Eight happy days of Hanuka.
Play, dance and sing, let voices ring,
Eight happy days of Hanuka.
Refrain

Children, Go Where I Send Thee

African American Spiritual
Arranged by James Rooker

2. Children, go where I send thee;
   How shall I send thee?
   I will send thee two by two.
   Well, two was the Paul and Silas,
   One was the little bitty baby,
   Wrapped in swaddling clothing,
   Lying in the manger.
   Born, born,
   Born in Bethlehem.

3. . . . I will send thee three by three.
   Well, three was the three men riding,
   Two was the Paul and Silas, . . .

4. . . . I will send thee four by four.
   Well, four was the four come a-knocking at the door,
   Three was the three men riding, . . .

5. . . . I will send thee five by five.
   Well, five was the Gospel preachers,
   Four was the four come a-knocking at the door, . . .

6. . . . I will send thee six by six.
   Well, six was the six that couldn't be fixed,
   Five was the Gospel preachers, . . .

7. . . . I will send thee seven by seven.
   Well, seven was the seven who went to heaven,
   Six was the six that couldn't be fixed, . . .

8. . . . I will send thee eight by eight.
   Well, eight was the eight who stood by the gate,
   Seven was the seven who went to heaven, . . .

9. . . . I will send thee nine by nine.
   Well, nine was the nine who saw the sign,
   Eight was the eight who stood by the gate, . . .

10. . . . I will send thee ten by ten.
    Well, ten was the Ten Commandments,
    Nine was the nine who saw the sign, . . .

Silent Night

Words by Joseph Mohr

Music by Franz Gruber

We Wish You a Merry Christmas

Carol from England
Arranged by James Harris

3. For we love our figgy pudding, *(3 times)*
So bring some out here.
Refrain

4. We won't leave until we get some, *(3 times)*
So bring some out here.
Refrain

Chrismus a Come

Traditional Song from Jamaica
Arranged by Jill Gallina

Almost Day

Folk Song from the United States
Arranged by Ting Ho

Sprightly

1. Chick - ens crow-in' for mid-night, it's al – most day,
Refrain: Chick - ens crow-in' for mid-night, it's al – most day,

Chick - ens crow-in' for mid-night, it's al – most day.
Chick - ens crow-in' for mid-night, it's al – most day.

2. Santa Claus is comin', it's almost day. . .
Refrain

3. Think I heard my ma say, it's almost day. . .
Refrain

4. Think I heard my pa say, it's almost day. . .
Refrain

La piñata

English Words by Alice Firgau

Folk Song from Mexico
Arranged by Martha Hilley

With excitement

VERSE

1. En las no - ches de po - sa – das, La pi - ña - ta es lo me -
1. On po - sa - da nights we have such fun, The pi - ña - ta is the

jor:_____ Aun las ni - ñas re - mil - ga_____ das Se an-i-man con gran fer -
best of all. E - ven shy girls join with ev - 'ry-one As we try to make it

2. Con tus ojitos vendados
   Y en las manos un bastón;
   ¡La olla rómpela a pedazos!
   ¡No le tengas compasión!
   Refrain

2. Put a blindfold over both your eyes,
   Take a stick in both your hands.
   Break the pot and let the pieces fly!
   Show no mercy, that's the plan!
   Refrain

Zumba, zumba

English Words by Margaret Marks

Folk Song from Spain
Arranged by Nicholas Zumbro

4

(clap)

blan - co ru - bio y co - lo - ra - do
Ev - 'ry - one brings him a pres - ent,

5

(clap)

que ha de ser el pas - tor - ci - to
Brings him a sa - vor - y meat - pie

6

D.C. al Fine

pa - ra cui - dar el ga - na - do.
Made out of par - tridge and pheas - ant. *(clap)*

Aguinaldo

English words courtesy of CP Language Institute, New York

Carol from Puerto Rico
Arranged by Buddy Skipper

5 REFRAIN

A la sa - len - de - ra,   A la sa - len - de - ra,
Oh, what joy I'm feel - ing,   O, what joy I'm feel - ing,

6

2nd time to Coda ⊕

A la sa - len - de - ra,   de mi co - ra - zón.
Oh, what joy I'm feel - ing   deep with - in my heart.

⊕ *Coda*

zón. _____
heart. _____

2. *Si no tiene nada*
   Si no tiene nada
   Nada nos dará;
   Pero lo que queremos
   cariño y bondad.
   Pero lo que queremos
   cariño y bondad.
   Refrain

2. If you've no possessions,
   If you've no possessions,
   Nothing can you share,
   But give love and kindness,
   Gifts beyond compare,
   But give love and kindness,
   Gifts beyond compare.
   Refrain

Habari Gani

Words and Music by James McBride
Arranged by Joseph Joubert

Lyrics:

1. Win - ter___ is here, so
2. Peace be___ un - to you,

Kwan - zaa___ is near, Cel - e - brat - ing joy and love as a
good things___ come true When you spread your joy and love in a

hap - py fam - i - ly. Join us in our greet - ing with
hap - py fam - i - ly. Self - de - ter - mi - na - tion,___

sev - en days of hol - i - day, Shar - ing all our gifts and love in a
liv - ing as a na - tion, too. We're all one re - la - tion and___

Ichi-gatsu tsuitachi (A New Year's Greeting)

Words by Senge Takatomi
English Words Adapted by Katherine S. Bolt

Music by Ue Sanemichi
School Song from Japan
Arranged by Bruce Simpson

Sincerely

To - shi no ha - ji - me no Ta - me - shi to - te
"O - me - de - to go - zai - mas," we will bow and say,

O - wa - ri na - ki yo no Me - de - ta - sa o
"O - me - de - to go - zai - mas," Hap - py New Year's Day.

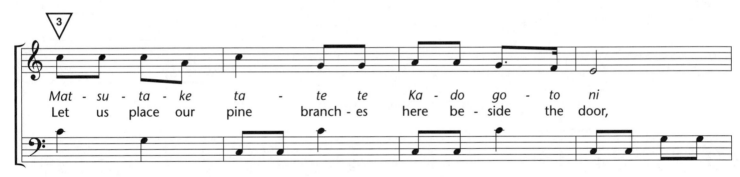

Mat - su - ta - ke ta - te te Ka - do go - to ni
Let us place our pine branch - es here be - side the door,

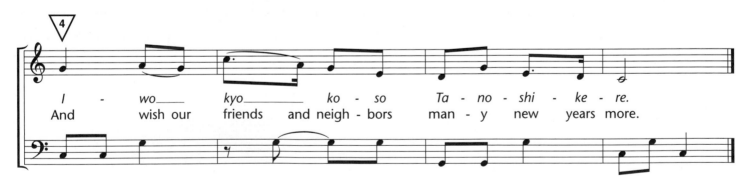

I - wo___ kyo___ ko - so Ta - no - shi - ke - re.
And wish our friends and neigh - bors man - y new years more.

174

Keep Your Eyes on the Prize

African American Freedom Song
Arranged by Joseph Joubert

3. Work all day and work all night,
   Tryin' to gain our civil rights.
   Keep your eyes on the prize.
   Hold on! *Refrain*

4. The only chain that a man can stand
   Is the chain of a hand in hand.
   Keep your eyes on the prize.
   Hold on! *Refrain*

Back of the Bus

Traditional Song
Adapted by Miss Mary Jane Pigee
Arranged by Joyce Kalbach

front of the bus,___ I'll be rid - in' up there.
driv - er's seat,___ I'll be driv - ing there.

America

Words by Samuel Francis Smith

Traditional Melody

Steadily

1. My coun - try! 'tis of thee, Sweet land of lib - er - ty,
2. My na - tive coun - try, thee, Land of the no - ble free,
3. Let mu - sic swell the breeze, And ring from all the trees

Of thee I sing; Land where my fa - thers died, Land of the
Thy name I love; I love thy rocks and rills, Thy woods and
Sweet Free - dom's song; Let mor - tal tongues a - wake, Let all that

Pil - grims' pride, From ev - 'ry___ moun - tain - side, Let___ free - dom ring!
tem - pled hills; My heart___ with___ rap - ture thrills Like___ that a - bove.
breathe par - take. Let rocks___ their___ si - lence break, The___ sound pro - long.

177

America, the Beautiful

Words by Katharine Lee Bates

Music by Samuel A. Ward

1. O beau-ti-ful for spa-cious skies, For am-ber waves of grain, For
2. O beau-ti-ful for pa-triot dream That sees be-yond the years For Thine

pur-ple moun-tain maj-es-ties A-bove the fruit-ed plain! A-
al-a-bas-ter cit-ies gleam, Un-dimmed by hu-man tears!

mer-i-ca! A-mer-i-ca! God shed His grace on thee And

crown thy good with broth-er-hood From sea to shin-ing sea!

Yankee Doodle

Words by Dr. Richard Schuckburgh

Traditional
Arranged by William Ward

With spirit

VERSE

1. Fath'r and I went down to camp, A - long with Cap - tain Good - in', And
2. And there we saw a thou - sand men, As rich as Squire_ Da - vid; And

there we saw the men and boys As thick as hast - y pud - din'.
what they wast - ed ev - 'ry day, I wish it could be sav - ed.

REFRAIN

Yan - kee Doo - dle, keep it up, Yan - kee Doo - dle dan - dy,

Mind the mu - sic and the step And with the girls be hand - y.

3. And there was Captain Washington
   Upon a slapping stallion,
   A-giving orders to his men;
   I guess there was a million. *Refrain*

The Star-Spangled Banner

Words by Francis Scott Key

Music by John Stafford Smith

1. Oh,__ say! can you see, by the dawn's ear - ly light, What so proud-ly we hailed at the

twi-light's last gleam - ing, Whose broad stripes and bright stars, through the per - il - ous fight, O'er the

ram - parts we watched were so gal-lan - tly stream-ing? And the rock - ets' red glare, the bombs

burst-ing in air. Gave proof through the night that our flag was still there Oh, say does that__

Star-Span-gled Ban - ner__ yet__ wave__ O'er the land__ of the free and the home of the brave?

CREDITS AND ACKNOWLEDGMENTS

Credit and appreciation are due publishers and copyright owners for use of the following:

4: "Hello to All the Children of the World", from *We Sing Around the World* by Pamela Conn Beall and Susan Hagen Nipp, copyright © 1994 by Pamela Conn Beall and Susan Hagen Nipp. Used by permission of Price Stern & Sloan, Inc., a division of Penguin Putnam Inc. 6: "Supercalifragilisticexpialidocious" Words and music by Richard M. Sherman and Robert B. Sherman. © 1963 Wonderland Music Company, Inc. All Rights Reserved. Reprinted by Permission. 8: "Gypsy in the Moonlight" (Folk Song from Trinidad), from *Caribbean Voyage: Brown Girl In The Ring*. Courtesy of the Alan Lomax Archives. 8: "Ding, Dong, Diggidiggidong" from *Music for Children,* Vol. 1, by Carl Orff and Gunild Keetman, English version adapted by Margaret Murray. Copyright © 1958 by Schott & Co., Ltd., London. Copyright renewed. All Rights Reserved. Used by permission of European American Distributors LLC, sole U.S. and Canadian agent for Schott & Co. Ltd., London. 9: "Golden Ring Around Susan Girl" folk song sung by Jean Ritchie, from *Folk Songs of the Southern Appalachians.* © 1963 Jean Ritchie Geordie Music Publishing Company. Used by permission. 10: "Ambos a dos" (Go Two by Two) English words © 1995 Silver Burdett Ginn. 11: "Joy To The World," Words and Music by Hoyt Axton. Copyright © 1970 by IRVING MUSIC, INC. Copyright Renewed. This arrangement Copyright © 2003 IRVING MUSIC, INC. All Rights Reserved. Used by Permission. 16: "Mud" from the poem, "Beavers in November" by Marilyn Singer from *Turtle in July*, (Simon & Schuster, 1989). Music © 2000 David Eddleman. All rights reserved. Reprinted by permission. 16: "Ida Red'" from *150 American Folk Songs to Sing Read and Play*. © Copyright 1974 by Boosey & Hawkes, Inc. Reprinted by permission of Boosey & Hawkes, Inc. 19: "La pulga de San José" © 1994 José-Luis Orozco, Spanish lyrics and English lyrics and musical arrangement. All rights reserved. Used by permission. Recordings for this selection and others by José-luis Orozco are available from Arcoris Records, P.O. Box 7482, Berkeley CA 94707. 20: "Peppermint Twist" Words and music by Joey Dee and Henry Glover. © 1961, 1962 (Copyrights Renewed) EMI Longitude Music Co. All Rights Reserved. Used by Permission. WARNER BROS. PUBLICATIONS U.S. INC., Miami, FL 33014. 24: "Ahora voy a cantarles" (Now Hear the Song I'll Sing You), from *Folk Songs of the Americas*, 1965, by Albert Lancaster Lloyd. Copyright © Novello & Co., Ltd. International Copyrights Secured. All Rights Reserved. Reprinted by Permission of G. Schirmer, Inc. (ASCAP). English version by Pearson Education, Inc. 24: "Mister Ram Goat-O" from *Brown Girl in The Ring* by Alan Lomax, J.D. Elder and Bess Lomax Hawes. Copyright © 1997 by Alan Lomax. Reprinted by permission of Pantheon Books, a division of Random House, Inc. 26: "John Kanaka" © 2002 Pearson Education, Inc. 26: "The Loco-Motion," Words and music by Gerry Goffin and Carole King. © 1962 (Renewed 1990) Screen Gems-EMI Music Inc. This arrangement © 2001 Screen Gems-EMI Music Inc. All Rights Reserved. International Copyright Secured. Used by permission. 28: "Family Tree" Words and music by John Forster and Tom Chapin. © 1988 Limousine Music Co. & The Last Music Co. (ASCAP) Reprinted by permission. 31: "I'm on My Way" © 2002 Pearson Education, Inc. 33: "Hej pada pada"(Dewdrops) Slovak lyrics and music by Marie Winn and Alan Miller from *The Fireside Book of Children's Songs*, published by Simon & Schuster, copyright 1966, renewed 1994. Reprinted by permission. English version by Pearson Education, Inc. Used with permission of Simon & Schuster. 34: "Let's Get the Rhythm of the Band", Warren-Mattox Productions: Music and lyrics from "Let's Get the Rhythm of the Band" in *Let's Get the Rhythm of the Band* by Cheryl Warren Mattox. Copyright © 1993 by Warren-Mattox Productions. Reprinted by permission. 36: "El gallo pinto (The Painted Rooster)" English words © 1995 Silver Burdett Ginn. 36: "Kingston Market," Words and Music by Irving Burgie. Copyright © 1960; Renewed 1988 Cherry Lane Music Publishing Company, Inc. (ASCAP), Lord Burgess Music Publishing (ASCAP) and DreamWorks Songs (ASCAP). This arrangement Copyright © 2003 Cherry Lane Music Publishing Company,

Inc. (ASCAP), Lord Burgess Music Publishing and DreamWorks Songs (ASCAP). Worldwide Rights for Lord Burgess Music Publishing and DreamWorks Songs Administered by Cherry Lane Music Publishing Company, Inc. International Copyright Secured. All Rights Reserved. Used by Permission. 36: "El gallo pinto (The Painted Rooster)" English words © 1995 Silver Burdett Ginn. 37: "Chicken on the Fence Post" from *A Book of Nonsense Songs* by Norman Cazdon. Used by permission. 40: "Never Smile at a Crocodile" Music by Jack Lawrence, words by Frank Churchill. © 1952 Walt Disney Music Company. All Rights Reserved. Reprinted by Permission. 41: "Hwa yuan li-de young wa wa" (Garden Lullaby) English words © 2002 Pearson Education, Inc. 43: "Had to Get Up This Morning" from *American Negro Songs and Spirituals* by John W. Work. Copyright © 1940, 1968 by Crown Publishers, Inc. Used by permission of Bonanza Books, a division of Random House, Inc. 44: "The Groundhog Blues" from *Music Play 25 Fun Lessons for Pre-K through 2nd Grade Classes* by Gayle Giese. © 1997 Belwin-Mills Publishing Corp. All Rights Reserved. Used by Permission. WARNER BROS. PUBLICATIONS U.S. INC., Miami, FL 33014. 44: "Tender Shepherd" (Count Your Sheep) from *Peter Pan*. Words by Carolyn Leigh, music by Mark Charlap. © 1954 Carolyn Leigh and Mark Charlap. © Renewed 1982 Carolyn Leigh and Mark Charlap. This arrangement Copyright © 2001 Carolyn Leigh and Mark Charlap. All rights on behalf of Mark Charlap Controlled by Edwin H. Morris & Company, a Division of MPL Communications, Inc. All Rights o/b/o Carolyn Leigh controlled and administered by EMI Carwin Catalog Inc. All Rights Reserved. Used by Permission. WARNER BROS. PUBLICATIONS U.S. INC., Miami, FL 33014 and Hal Leonard Corporation. 46: "Draw Me a Bucket of Water" from *Step It Down* Written and adapted by Bessie Jones. Collected and edited by Alan Lomax. TRO–Copyright 1972 (Renewed) Ludlow Music, Inc., New York, New York. Used by Permission. 48: "The Juniper Tree" Copyright 1937 by John A. Lomax. Reprinted by permission of Global Jukebox Publishing. 49: "¡Que gusto!" (What Pleasure!) English words by Ruth DeCesare. © Alfred Publishing Co., Inc. Used with permission of the publisher. 50: "Doong gul ge" ('Round and Around We Go). English words © 2002 Pearson Education, Inc. 52: "Kum bachur atzel" (Hear the Rooster Crowing) English words © 2002 Pearson Education, Inc. 54: "Hop Up, My Ladies" Collected, adapted and arranged by John A. Lomax and Alan Lomax. TRO © Copyright 1941 (Renewed) Ludlow Music, Inc., New York, NY. Used by permission. 57: "Michael Finnigan" © 2002 Pearson Education, Inc. 58: "Each of Us Is a Flower," Charlotte Diamond Music SOCAN as recorded by Charlotte Diamond on 10 Carrot Diamond. Reprinted by permission. 60: "The Flat Foot Floogee" words and music by Slim Gaillard, Bud Green, and Slam Stewart. © 1938 (Renewed) by Jewel Music Publishing Co., Inc. (ASCAP) in the United States. This arrangement Copyright © 2001 by Jewel Music Publishing Co., Inc. (ASCAP) Holliday Publications (ASCAP) and O Vouti Publishing (ASCAP) in the United States. All Rights for O Vouti Publishing Administered by Quartet Music, Inc. International Copyright Secured. All Rights Reserved. Used by permission. 66: "Don't Let Your Watch Run Down" from *South Texas Work Songs* by Gates Thomas, found in Publications of the Texas Folklore Society No. V, 1926, titled Rainbow in the Morning. Reprinted with permission. 68: "Waltzing With Bears" Words and music by Dale Marxen. © 1986 Dale Marxen. Used by permission of author. 70: "Railroad Corral" from *Springboards: Ideas for Music* by Belle Farmer. Nelson Thomson Learning. Used by permission. 72: "Now Let Me Fly" © 1995 Silver Burdett Ginn. 74: "Don't Let the Wind" from *The Kodaly Context* by Lois Choksy. © 1981 by Prentice-Hall, Inc. Reprinted by permission of Pearson Education, Inc., Upper Saddle River, NJ. 74: "Erdö, erdö de magos"(In the Silent Forest) English words © 1991 Silver Burdett Ginn. 75: "Good Morning" Words and music by Elizabeth Gilpatrick. © 1996 Alfred Publishing Co., Inc. Used with permission of the publisher. 76: "I'd Like To Teach The World To Sing (In Perfect Harmony)" Words and Music by: Bill Backer, Billy Davis, Roger Cook, Roger Greenaway. © 1971 Shada Music Co., Inc.

CREDITS AND ACKNOWLEDGMENTS *continued*

CREDITS AND ACKNOWLEDGMENTS *continued*

The editors of Scott Foresman have made every attempt to verify the source of "I Don't Care If the Rain Comes Down" (p. 14), "Black Snake" (p. 23), "El gallo pinto (The Painted Rooster)" (p. 36), "Old Man Mosie" (p. 42), "Doong gul ge ('Round and Around We Go)" (p. 50), "Shu ha mo (Frogs)" (p. 105), and "El sapito (Little Toad)" (p. 127), but were unable to do so.

The editors of Scott Foresman and Company have made every effort to locate all copyright holders of material used in this book. If any errors or omissions have occurred, corrections will be made.

Song Index

A Ram Sam Sam 80
Aguinaldo 170
Ah, eu entrei na roda (I Came to Try This Game) 117
Ahora voy a cantarles (Now Hear the Song I'll Sing You) 24
Al ánimo 121
Al citrón 120
Al tambor (The Drum Song) 102
Alabama Gal 42
Almost Day 166
Ambos a dos (Go Two by Two) 13
America 177
America, the Beautiful 178
Artsa alinu (Come to the Land) 108
Au clair de la lune (In the Moonlight) 10

Back of the Bus 176
Big Beautiful Planet 122
Bird Song (*Sarika keo*) 104
Black Snake 23
Bling Blang 92
Bluebonnets of Texas 124
Bonavist' Harbour 111

Chanukah Games 160
Chicken on the Fence Post 37
Children, Go Where I Send Thee 162
Chrismus a Come 165
Coffee Grows on White Oak Trees 67
Come to the Land (*Artsa alinu*) 108

Dewdrops (*Hej pada pada*) 33
Ding, Dong, Diggidiggidong 8
Do, Lord 64
Don Gato 138
Don't Let the Wind 74
Don't Let Your Watch Run Down 68
Don't Want to Know You (*Nie chce cie znác*) 119
Doong gul ge ('Round and Around We Go) 50
Draw Me a Bucket of Water 46
Drum Song, The (*Al tambor*) 102

Each of Us Is a Flower 58
El barquito (The Tiny Boat) 140
El gallo pinto (The Painted Rooster) 36
El mes de abril (The Month of April) 123
El rabel (The Violin) 142
El sapito (The Little Toad) 127
Erdö, erdö de magos (In the Silent Forest) 74

Family Tree 28
Flat Foot Floogee, The 60
Four White Horses 116
Frogs (*Shu ha mo*) 105

Garden Lullaby (*Hwa yuan li-de young wa wa*) 41
Go Two by Two (*Ambos a dos*) 13
Go with the Music and Sing 152
Golden Ring Around Susan 9
Good Morning 75
Great Day 25
Groundhog Blues, The 44
Gypsy in the Moonlight 8

Habari Gani 172
Had to Get Up This Mornin' Soon 43
Halloween Is a Very Unusual Night 156
Hama chi dori (Plovers) 126
Hanuka, Hanuka 161
Happy Birthday (*Mübärak*) 107
Hashkediya (*Tu b'Shvat* Is Here) 79
He's Got the Whole World in His Hands 85
Hear the Rooster Crowing (*Kum bachur atzel*) 52
Hej pada pada (Dewdrops) 33
Hello to All the Children of the World 4
Hevenu shalom aleichem (We Come to Greet You in Peace) 154
Hop Up, My Ladies 54
Hot Cross Buns (Version 1) 82
Hot Cross Buns (Version 2) 82
Hush, Hush 62
Hwa yuan li-de young wa wa (Garden Lullaby) 41

I Came to Try This Game (*Ah, eu entrei na roda*) 117
I Don't Care If the Rain Comes Down 14
I Wonder Where Maria's Gone 120
I'd Like to Teach the World to Sing 76
I'm on My Way 31
I've Been Working on the Railroad 90
Ichi-gatsu tsuitachi (A New Year's Greeting) 174
Ida Red 16
If a Tiger Calls 139
In the Moonlight (*Au clair de la lune*) 10
In the Pumpkin Patch 155
In the Silent Forest (*Erdö, erdö de magos*) 74

It's a Beautiful Day 128
It's a Small World 101

Jan ken pon 115
John Kanaka 26
Joy to the World 11
Juniper Tree, The 48

Karangatia ra 103
Keep Your Eyes on the Prize 175
Kingston Market 36
Knock No More 159
Kum bachur atzel (Hear the Rooster Crowing) 52

La calle ancha (The Wide Street) 113
La paloma blanca (The White Dove) 96
La piñata 166
La pulga de San José 19
Let's Celebrate! 150
Let's Get the Rhythm of the Band 34
Let's Go to the Sea (*Vamos a la mar*) 83
Li'l Liza Jane 53
Little Johnny Brown 118
Little Toad, The (*El sapito*) 127
Loco-Motion, The 26
Look Out for Mother Earth 130
Love Somebody 38
Lovely Hala Trees (*Nani wale na hala*) 98

Make New Friends 18
May the Sun Shine Forever (*Pust' 'vsegda budet sonse*) 106
Michael Finnigan 57
Mister Ram Goat-O 24
Month of April, The (*El mes de abril*) 123
Morning Is Come 47
Mübärak (Happy Birthday) 107
Mud 16

Nani wale na hala (Lovely Hala Trees) 98
Never Smile at a Crocodile 40
New Year's Greeting, A (*Ichi-gatsu tsuitachi*) 174
Nie chcę cię znác (Don't Want to Know You) 119
Now Hear the Song I'll Sing You (*Ahora voy a cantarles*) 24
Now Let Me Fly 72

SONG INDEX *continued*

Oh, Won't You Sit Down 14
Old Dan Tucker 39
Old Man Mosie 42
Old Texas 32
One Morning Soon 30
Over the River and Through the
  Wood 158

Painted Rooster, The (*El gallo pinto*)
  36
Peace Like a River 94
Peppermint Twist 20
Plovers (*Hama chi dori*) 116
Poco, Le' Me 'Lone 114
Pretty Saro 81
Pust' 'vsegda budet sonse (May the
  Sun Shine Forever) 106

¡Qué gusto! (What Pleasure) 49

Railroad Corral 70
Rockin' Robin 146
'Round and Around We Go (*Doong
  gul ge*) 50

Sansaw akroma 109
Sarika keo (Bird Song) 104
Shu ha mo (Frogs) 105
Sierra Morena 112
Silent Night 163
Sing, America, Sing! 86
Sing Your Story 136
Small Job, A 82
Song of One, A 134
Song of the Fishes 93
St. Patrick Was a Gentleman 110
Star-Spangled Banner, The 180
Supercalifragilisticexpialidocious 6
Sweet Potatoes 84

Take Me Out to the Ball Game 99
Tender Shepherd 44
Texas Cowboy 95
This Old Man 56
Tiny Boat, The (*El barquito*) 140
Train Is A-Comin' 23
Tu b'Shvat Is Here (*Hashkediya*) 79
Turn the Glasses Over 78

Vamos a la mar (Let's Go to the Sea)
  83
Violin, The (*El rabel*) 142

Walk Together, Children 56
Waltzing with Bears 68
We Come to Greet You in Peace
  (*Hevenu shalom aleichem*) 154
We Wish You a Merry Christmas 164
We've Got Lots in Common 144
What Pleasure (*¡Qué gusto!*) 49
White Dove, The (*La paloma
  blanca*) 96
Wide Street, The (*La calle ancha*)
  113
Wooly Bully 148
World We Love, The 132

Yankee Doodle 179
You're a Grand Old Flag 100

Zumba, Zumba 168

NOTE: These page numbers refer
to the actual page in this book.
Page numbers for the Pupil Edition
appear above the title of each
arrangement.